D1268373

WILLIAM HERSCHEL

by the same author

DIRECTION FINDING BY THE STARS

INTRODUCING ASTRONOMY

AMATEUR ASTRONOMER'S HANDBOOK

OBSERVATIONAL ASTRONOMY FOR AMATEURS

(Faber and Faber)

THE HEAVENS ABOVE: A RATIONALE
OF ASTRONOMY

(Oxford University Press)

*

editor

THE SHORTER POEMS OF WALTER SAVAGE LANDOR

(Cambridge University Press)

*

translator

THE EXPANSION OF THE UNIVERSE

by Paul Couderc

(Faber and Faber)

WILLIAM HERSCHEL, AGED 46

WILLIAM HERSCHEL

Explorer of the Heavens

by

J. B. SIDGWICK

FABER AND FABER LIMITED

24 Russell Square

London

First published in mcmliii
by Faber and Faber Limited
24 Russell Square London W.C.1
Printed in Great Britain by
Latimer Trend & Co Ltd Plymouth

CONTENTS

William Herschel [illegible] L. F. Ab[illegible]
bott in the National Portrait Gallery [illegible]
C. A. Lubbock, *The Herschel Chronicle*, Cambridge University Press)

Caroline Herschel in her old age [illegible] in the
National Gallery of Hanover. By kind permission of Lady
Herschel)

The Forty-Foot Telescope [illegible]
(*Philosophical Transactions*)

An island universe [illegible]
what our own Galaxy might [illegible] if seen at a very
great distance from a viewpoint [illegible]
plane (Photograph by [illegible])

PLATES

'I will make such telescopes, and see such things.'

★

'I have looked further into space than ever human being did before me.'

Coelorum perrupit claustra: 'He broke through the barriers of the heavens.'

'I will make such telescopes, and see such things.' (1782)

'I have looked further into space than ever human being did before me.' (1813)

Coelorum perrupit claustra: He burst through the barriers of the heavens. (1822)

THE FRAMEWORK OF WILLIAM HERSCHEL'S LIFE

1738	Born at Hanover, November 15th
1753	Joined the regimental band of the Hanoverian Guard
1757	Settled in England
1760	Started musical work in the north of England
1766	Moved to Bath
1772	Joined at Bath by his sister, Caroline
1773	First attempts at telescope making
1781	Discovery of Uranus
1782	Moved to Datchet, as astronomer under Royal patronage
1786	Moved to Slough
1788	Marriage to Mary Pitt
1789	Forty-foot telescope completed
1792	John Herschel born, March 7th
1793	Naturalized
1802	Paris visit
1815	Last observations with the forty-foot telescope
1816	Knighthood of the Hanoverian Guelphic Order
1821	President of the Astronomical Society
1822	Died at Slough, August 25th

THE FRAMEWORK OF WILLIAM HERSCHEL'S LIFE

1738	Born at Hanover, November 15th
1753	Joined the regimental band of the Hanoverian Guards
1757	Settled in London
1760	Started musical work in the north of England
1766	Moved to Bath, as Octagon Chapel organist
1772	Joined at Bath by his sister Caroline
1773	First attempts at telescope making
1781	Discovery of Uranus
1782	Moved to Datchet, as astronomer under Royal patronage
1786	Moved to Slough
1788	Marriage to Mary Pitt
1789	Forty-foot telescope completed
1792	John Herschel born, March 7th
1793	Naturalized
1802	Paris visit
1815	Last observations with the forty-foot telescope
1816	Knighthood in the Hanoverian Guelphic Order
1821	President of the Astronomical Society
1822	Died at Slough, August 25th

CHAPTER ONE

BOYHOOD, AND LIFE IN GERMANY

The underlying patterns of men's lives make a fascinating study, for they are as various as Man himself. Some describe a course from the cradle to the grave that is as direct and unswerving as the flight of an arrow. The life-lines of others are disjointed, contorted, diverted by chance encounters and accidents till any semblance of pattern is lost beneath a tangle of apparent irrelevancies.

William Herschel, and his son John, curiously illustrate this theme. John was born in an astronomical household and devoted his life to astronomy: his career was of the arrow-flight variety. Looked at in retrospect, it gives the impression of being pre-ordained by his birth and environment—a straight line which he followed undeviatingly to the end. With his father it was very different. How did it come about that William Herschel, who was born in Hanover the son of an obscure military bandsman, and who likewise started life as a professional musician, became finally one of the world's greatest observational astronomers, the discoverer of Uranus, the personal astronomer of George III at Windsor, and one who did as much to widen the vistas of Man's universe as, in his different field, did Darwin?

BOYHOOD, AND LIFE IN GERMANY

The circumstances of few great men's lives have differed so widely at their outset and at their conclusion as that of William Herschel. Yet the basic pattern of his career is simple enough, and the transformation of the unknown German bandsman into the world-famous English astronomer was direct and logical. During his youth the outward circumstances of his life suffered many vicissitudes, it is true; and it might be argued that if, for instance, the French had been defeated in the Battle of Hastenbeck, Herschel would never have become an astronomer—that, in fact, his ultimate achievements were the result of chance experiences and historical accidents over which he had no control. But to do so would be misleading, for despite the varied and adventurous nature of his early years, during which he seemed to be buffeted to and fro by aimless circumstance, the true pattern of his life was as unerring as that of his son's; he simply had a greater distance to travel.

Each step in his development followed logically from its predecessor in a progression which seems to have been unalterably determined. His work as a practising musician demanded that he should learn the theory of music; to do this he had to study and improve his grasp of mathematics; this captured his imagination and led him on far beyond the point that his musical understanding required; it led him, in fact, to the study of optics; from his study of theoretical optics was born the desire to construct a telescope of his own, for Herschel was of a practical turn of mind, and a natural mechanician; what he saw with his first telescope fired his astronomer's imagination. . . . From then on his course was clear, and all his subsequent achievements flowed smoothly from his genius. One of the strongest impressions one receives on reading the life of Herschel is that from start to finish he was swept along by a deep and steady-flowing current.

BOYHOOD, AND LIFE IN GERMANY

Friedrich Wilhelm Herschel[1] was born at Hanover on 15th November 1738. His ancestry was humble: his father, Isaac, was a musician; his paternal grandfather had been a successful master-gardener; and his great-grandfather a brewer. At the time of William's birth Isaac had been an oboeist in the band of the Hanoverian Foot Guards for seven years, and married for six. He and his wife Anna produced a family of respectable size, William having five brothers and sisters who lived to adulthood. Of these, Sophia and Jacob were older than he was.

The key to an understanding of how William's remarkable gifts sprang from a comparatively unremarkable soil lies largely in the person and character of his father. Isaac Herschel had inherited from his father a love of music but none of gardening. Orphaned in childhood, he had at an early age taught himself to play the violin by ear, and he determined to devote his life to music. At the age of twenty-one he turned his back for ever on gardening as a profession, concentrated on his musical studies, and in 1731 came to Hanover, where he was at once engaged as oboeist in the band of the Guards regiment. He was an accomplished musician and, more than that, a man of liberal imagination and wide-ranging interests. Many years later Caroline, William's younger sister, described how her father 'was a great admirer of astronomy, and had some knowledge of that science, for I remember his taking me, on a clear frosty night, into the street, to make me acquainted with several of the most beautiful constellations, after we had been gazing at a comet which was then visible. And I well remember with what delight he used to assist my Brother William in his various contrivances in the pursuit of his philosophical studies, among which was a neatly turned

[1] It was not till his naturalization in 1793 that he took the single name, William, by which he is now invariably known.

4-inch globe, upon which the equator and ecliptic were engraved by my Brother.'

Though Isaac's position as bandsman and teacher never earned him enough to supply his growing family with more than the bare domestic necessities, he was determined that they should at least have the benefit of his musical knowledge and ability. He also did what he could to stimulate their imaginations and awaken in them an appreciation of the things of the mind. All his children, with the sole exception of Sophia, did in fact develop considerable musical talent, and four of them took up music as their profession. William himself in later years recollected how, at the age of four, his father set him on a table to play a violin solo on a special miniature instrument that had been made for him.

All the children were in turn sent to the Garrison school in Hanover, where they received at any rate the dry bones of an education—the three 'Rs', with a fourth, Religion, thrown in for good measure. William soon displayed indications of an intellect above the average, and the master would sometimes set him to hear the lessons of the younger pupils—particularly in arithmetic, at which he excelled.

During the first eight years of William's life the Herschel home can have seen little of Isaac. Frederick II had acceded to the Prussian throne in 1740, and, hell-bent on qualifying for the title of 'the Great', had invaded Silesia the following year, thus precipitating Europe into twelve years of war. England sided with Prussia against a Franco-Austrian alliance, and during the next few years Isaac Herschel's engagement with the Guards band did not allow him more than spasmodic visits to his family.

In 1743, after the Battle of Dettingen, he was forced to pass the night in a waterlogged ditch, an experience which undermined his always rather weak constitution, and sowed the seeds of the asthma and rheumatism from which he suffered for the rest of his life. In 1746 he returned home, however, and life in the Herschel household took on a brighter aspect.

But whatever joy may have sprung from the reunion of the family, they were beset by chronic financial troubles. Isaac supplemented his bandsman's earnings by taking private pupils, but the economics of the household did not take a real turn for the better until 1753; in that year William, who had left the Garrison school the previous year, became engaged as violinist and oboeist in the Guards band, and his elder brother Jacob was appointed organist at the Garrison church. Their earnings made it possible for Isaac to arrange for a certain Hofschläger to give them tuition in French. Hofschläger appears to have been a man of some attainment, and he took a great liking to William, whom he encouraged in the cultivation of those wider interests that Isaac had already aroused in his son—in particular, philosophy, logic and ethics. Referring to his friendship with Hofschläger, William later wrote, 'To this fortunate circumstance it was undoubtedly owing, that altho' I loved music to excess and made considerable progress in it, I yet determined with a sort of enthusiasm to devote every moment I could spare to the pursuit of knowledge, which I regarded as the sovereign good, and in which I resolved to place all my future views of happiness in life.' Already it is possible to discern in William the germination of trends that were to carry him so far beyond the orbit of an instrumentalist in a German military band.

Though William's technical education may have been somewhat sparse and primitive by modern standards, the influence of his father and of Hofschläger was of the utmost value to him. If education is less a matter of memory-training than the fostering of an alert and receptive intelligence and the cultivation of a love of knowledge for its own sake, then it may truly be said that William Herschel's education was not neglected.

At this period, when William was about sixteen, both he and Jacob were from time to time playing with the Court orchestra, either as soloists or as assistants, and a passage in the memoirs of Caroline (then a girl of four) throws an interesting light on William's home background. 'I remember that I was frequently prevented from going to sleep by the lively criticism on music . . . or conversations on philosophical subjects which lasted frequently till morning, in which my father was a lively partaker. . . . Generally their conversation would branch out on philosophical subjects, when my Brother William and my father often argued with such warmth, that my mother's interference became necessary, when the names Leibnitz, Newton and Euler sounded rather too loud for the repose of her little ones, who ought to be in school by seven in the morning. But it seems that on the brothers retiring to their own room, where they shared the same bed, my Brother William had still a great deal to say; and frequently it happened that when he stopped for an assent or reply, he found his hearer was gone to sleep, and I suppose it was not till then that he bethought himself to do the same.'

But the Hanoverians' respite from the wars was of short duration. In 1755 hostilities broke out again between England and France; Prussia sided with England; Austria and Russia came in with the French; and by the following spring, with the Seven Years' War well under way, apprehension in England that a French invasion was imminent had reached such a pitch that the Hanoverian Guards were ordered overseas to reinforce the English defences. With them went their regimental band, and bandsmen Isaac, Jacob and William Herschel. This was William's first visit to the country he was later to make his home, and although his stay was short—the

French scare had died down sufficiently for the Guards to return to Germany in the autumn—he made the acquaintance of families in Coxheath, Maidstone and Rochester who were to be of assistance to him two years later when he was establishing his roots in his adopted homeland. He also took advantage of the enforced visit to work hard at English—a language of which, when he landed at Chatham in April 1756, he spoke not a single word.

William Herschel's life was now approaching the first of its two important encounters with 'accident'—encounters which were to transform the outward circumstances of his life though they left its fundamental direction unaltered. In the spring of 1757, only a few months after the regiment's return from England, the campaign opened which in July culminated with the defeat of the combined Hessian and Hanoverian troops under the Duke of Cumberland at Hastenbeck, a town some twenty-five miles from Hanover. During the campaigning that led up to this battle William repeated his father's earlier experiences of wet ditches and sodden ploughland as sleeping places, but the Battle of Hastenbeck was, so far as we know, the only occasion on which the philosophically inclined bandsman was near enough to the fighting to come actually under fire. 'During the battle,' John Herschel wrote many years later, remembering a remark of his father's, 'with balls flying over his head he walked behind a hedge spouting speeches, rhetoric being then his favourite study.'

That William's heart was not in his military career would be stating the case mildly, and when his father recommended him to consider his own safety and return to Hanover, he was willing enough to follow the advice. He dismisses the affair casually enough in the Biographical Memorandums which he wrote later in life: 'About the time of the Battle of Hastenbeck (July 26) we were so near the field of action as to be within the reach of gunshot; when this happened my father advised me to look to my own safety. Accordingly I left the engagement and took the road to Hanover.'

At home, however, he found his position if anything more perilous than with the now disabled Hanoverian troops. Hanover had not yet been occupied by the French, and the citizens were making frantic last-minute attempts to raise an extempore Home Guard for its defence. All unengaged young men—even the clergy—were liable for these duties, and since he was not technically a soldier William might at any moment have been detected and pressed into service. For a short time he remained in hiding in his home, and then decided to rejoin his regiment. Caroline, in her Memoirs, tells how '. . . I had only a passing glimpse of my Brother as I was sitting at the entrance to our street door, when he glided like a shadow along, wrapped in a greatcoat, followed by my mother with a parcel containing his accoutrements. After he had succeeded in passing unnoticed beyond the last sentinel at Herrenhausen he changed his dress.'

Apparently the treatment of absentees without leave was more lenient in the Hanoverian army two hundred years ago than is common nowadays, for he seems to have suffered no reprisals when he reported once more for duty. Conditions in the defeated army were probably too chaotic for the addition or subtraction of one young oboe-player to excite much comment. William himself remarked that 'When I had rejoined the regiment I found that nobody had time to look after the musicians; they did not seem to be wanted.' So superfluous were they, indeed, that within two months he again quitted the regiment. This time it was for good.

He was, as before, urged upon this course by his father, who gave it as his opinion that owing to William's youth when he joined the band he had never been properly sworn in, and was therefore at liberty to leave the service as and when he liked. The doings of the regiment's musicians were still a matter of indifference to those in authority, and William had no difficulty in slipping away unnoticed. He made first for Hamburg, where he was joined by his brother Jacob: Hanover had by then been occupied by the French, and was to remain so for two more years. By November the two brothers were in London, and except for an occasional short visit William was never to see his homeland again.

For more than a century following these events it was commonly supposed that Herschel was technically a deserter from the army, and that he received a special pardon from George III twenty-five years later, so that he might without impropriety accept the king's patronage. That such an interpretation was, to say the least, improbable, should have been obvious from the fact that during these years William paid three visits to Hanover quite openly—a risk he would hardly have taken had he been a proscribed deserter. In fact, Isaac had kept the promise he had made at the time of William's flight to Hamburg, and had obtained his official discharge for him. In 1912 Dreyer published in his introduction to *The Scientific Papers of Sir William Herschel* a copy of this certificate of discharge, signed by General Spörcken and dated 1762. It is clear, therefore, that the authorities did not regard William as a deserter, and it is interesting in this connection to note that the word 'soldier' in the printed discharge papers is crossed out, and 'oboeist' written in by hand. He was never a deserter for the simple reason that he had never technically been a soldier.

William Herschel's military career, if it did not culminate in a blaze of glory, at least did not end in the ignominy of desertion.

CHAPTER TWO

ESTABLISHING ROOTS IN ENGLAND

The two brothers—William just nineteen, and Jacob four years older—arrived in England practically penniless but not, thanks to their visit with the Guards the previous year, entirely friendless. They made straight for London where William applied to a music shop for copying work and dealt so swiftly with his first commission, an opera, that from then onward he was assured of as much work as he required to support himself until something better fitting his talents should come along. Jacob, for his part, took up teaching.

Except that William was hard put to it to make ends meet, little is known of the circumstances of his life during those first two difficult years in London. In 1759 a vacancy occurred in the Court orchestra at Hanover, and Jacob returned in the hope (which was justified) of filling it. William always had the highest regard for Jacob, both as a musician and as a brother, and after his departure he carried on the copious correspondence with him in German, English and French which is the main source of our knowledge of his life during the subsequent few years. Though William must have been saddened at this breaking of his sole link with his homeland, the year 1759 was nevertheless a happy one for the family he had left behind; for it saw the return not only of the eldest son but also of the father: with the coming of peace, after the Battle of Minden, Isaac Herschel was released from the Guards band and was officially discharged the following year. His health, however, had been ruined by his military experiences, and acute financial difficulties followed in the train of his inability to undertake work as a performer.

William's fortunes, on the other hand, were soon to take a turn for the better. In 1760 Lord Darlington, having heard good accounts of the young German musician, appointed William instructor to the band of the Durham Militia, of which he was Colonel. This appointment suited Herschel very well since he had already reached the conclusion that London was glutted with musicians and that he would have to try his luck in the provinces; the engagement was, moreover, on a monthly basis, which meant that he would not be tied if and when something better presented itself. Accordingly he transferred himself and his few belongings from London to the north and took lodgings in Sunderland, where he remained for the two years during which he retained Lord Darlington's appointment.

Training the bandsmen was by no means his only occupation. As his attainments became known he found himself increasingly in demand both as a private teacher and as a performer. This involved him in considerable and fairly continuous travelling, which he undertook on horseback; often he covered as many as fifty miles in a day, and his work was no sinecure during the bleak winter months. In one of his letters to Jacob he describes what must have been a by no means unusual experience: 'If I found any pleasure in showing myself in a situation calling for pity, I would dilate on my experiences of the past night. However, without indulging myself so far, I will only say that at 9 o'clock, when I still had about 20 miles to ride, I was caught in an unusually heavy thunderstorm, which continued, accompanied by torrents of rain, with unbroken fury for three hours, and threatened me with sudden death. The distance from an inhabitation, the darkness and loneliness, obliged me nevertheless to ride on. I pursued my way therefore with unshaken sangfroid although I was often obliged to shut my eyes on account of the blinding lightning. At last the flashes all around me were so terrifying that my horse refused to go on; luckily at this moment I found myself near a house, into which, after much knocking, I was admitted. This morning, at 3 o'clock, I proceeded on my journey and arrived safely at this place.'

One of the houses that he was visiting at this time was the home of Sir Ralph Milbanke at Halnaby, and it was here that in 1761 he made his first personal contact with a member of the Royal Family which was to play such an important role in his later life: 'Now I must make you a little story about what I have done this week. My vanity has been a little flattered, for I had a message by a courier from Lady M. requesting my presence. I hastened thither and found at Halnaby the Duke of York, the King's brother. We made music for the whole week as his Royal Highness plays the violincello very well. I had therefore the honour not only to play several solos with his approval but to be accompanied by him.'

Composition, rather than teaching or performing, was William's chief interest and ambition, and during these years in Yorkshire he found time from his other duties to compose in considerable quantities: he records in one letter that within the short period from June 1760 to January 1761 he had completed no less than seven symphonies—though these were probably short orchestral pieces rather than symphonies as we now use the term, for even Mozart at his most prolific barely achieved seven symphonies in six months.[1] At the same time William was reading and studying in a wide range of subjects unconnected with music; the love of knowledge and the breadth of interests that he owed to his father and his old French teacher made it impossible for him ever to be satisfied with the narrow outlook and restricted horizons of the specialist. Many of his letters to Jacob are concerned wholly with philosophical and theological speculations (though as many, or more, deal exclusively with his and Jacob's compositions, and with the technique of their common profession), and his reading included such authors as Locke, Epictetus and Leibnitz.

It will be remembered that as a schoolboy William showed some natural aptitude for arithmetic. He lacked the makings of a brilliant mathematician—his son John far surpassed him in this respect—but his talent was adequate to his later needs. A crucially important step in the unfolding of the Herschel story is referred to by William in a letter to Dr. Hutton concerning this period of his life. After remarking that his leisure was largely given to the study of English, Italian and Latin (Greek he had to abandon as taking up too much of his time!), he went on: 'The theory of music being connected with mathematics had induced me very early to read in Germany all what had been written upon the subject of harmony; and when not long after my arrival in England the valuable book of Dr. Smith's Harmonics came into my hands, I perceived

[1] At the age of sixteen Mozart wrote in a single year (which was also the year of Caroline Herschel's coming to England) 10 symphonies, 2 operas, 6 string quartets, 4 orchestral divertimenti, 4 large-scale works for organ, orchestra and voices (including a Mass), 2 sonatas for organ and strings, 1 piano sonata, 6 minuets, and 6 songs. Perhaps the most astonishing example of human creativity that the world has seen.

my ignorance and had recourse to other authors for information, by which I was drawn on from one branch of mathematics to another.' The importance of this new direction to his studies lay in the fact that, 'from one branch of mathematics to another', he was led to optics—and optics was the gateway by which Herschel entered astronomy.

In 1761 he heard that the manager of concerts in Edinburgh was intending to retire, and somewhat rashly resigned his position with the Durham militia and set off for Edinburgh to apply for the post. On his way he stopped at Newcastle, where he played as first violinist and soloist at a subscription concert. He was doomed to disappointment in Edinburgh, however, for on his arrival he learnt that the concert director had changed his mind about retiring. The visit was not entirely wasted, for he played as leader at a concert in which some of his own works ('symphonies and solo concertos') were performed. He also made the acquaintance of Hume, the empiricist philosopher, who praised his concert and invited him to dinner where he was introduced to a large company of the local celebrities.

After the Edinburgh fiasco Herschel returned south, and for the next few months was kept busy with temporary engagements at Newcastle, Pontefract and elsewhere. This relapse into insecurity weighed heavily on his spirits, and in a mood of deep depression he considered returning to Germany. He was finally restrained from doing so by the fact that even as a wandering teacher and occasional performer his prospects in England were better than in Hanover; this was a matter of importance to him, less for his own sake than because he was helping his father by sending him a part of his earnings. William was by nature warm-hearted and affectionate, and he felt very strongly the ties and responsibilities that linked him to his home. Not only did he help his father over a number of years following the latter's discharge from the Guards, but at various times he showed his generosity towards one or other of his brothers; and when, some years later, his younger brother Dietrich ran away from home, he did not hesitate to drop his work in England in order to follow his trail round the Continent.

Early in 1762 the tide turned in William's favour again, and he was offered the post of concert manager in Leeds. This post—which he held for four years—seems to have involved the organization of each season's programme of concerts, as well as the training, rehearsing and conducting of the orchestra. (In those days it was usual for an orchestra to be conducted by the first violin, rather than by a separate conductor.) During this time he made Leeds his headquarters, lodging with a couple named Bulman who became such firm friends that they later followed him to Bath where a combined household was once again set up. William's peripatetic days were not yet over, however, for we find him visiting musical families at Doncaster, Halifax, Pontefract and other northern centres, while still carrying out his duties at Leeds.

In the year of his move to Leeds, William's official discharge from the Hanoverian army was issued. He did not immediately set out for Hanover since he wanted to accumulate sufficient savings to allow him to make the visit without being a burden to his chronically hard-pressed family, and it was not until the spring of 1764 that he once again saw his old home, after an absence of nearly seven years.

It is easy to believe that it was a joyful reunion—Caroline speaks of the 'Tumult of joy' into which they were thrown. There was nevertheless a sadder side to it. The intervening years had been hard on Isaac. His health had been ruined by the hardships he had undergone during his long years of campaigning. The needs of his family allowed him no respite from toil when he might with gratitude have gone into a peaceful retirement.

When, after a stay of only a fortnight, William bade farewell to his father it was for the last time. Soon afterwards Isaac had a stroke, from which he never fully recovered, and three years later he died. Isaac Herschel had been a wise and affectionate father, and his part in the development of those qualities in his son which were to lead him so far from the humble musician's house in Hanover, is not to be underrated.

On his return to England Herschel fell once more into the busy routine of his life, and so continued for a couple of years nursing the Leeds orchestra and travelling continuously between Leeds, Halifax, Pontefract, Doncaster, Warrington and other towns where his services as teacher or performer were required. In 1766 he moved to Halifax, where a new church organ was being built and where a competition was to be held later in the year to select an organist. There is no record that Herschel had ever previously played the instrument, but he practised to such good effect that he was able to carry on for the resident organists at Halifax and Wakefield while they were on their summer holidays. There had been considerable opposition to the installation of the new organ: to the puritanically minded section of the community it was a 'heathenish thing'. The dispute was eventually brought to the courts for decision, pending which the organ could not be used. However the matter was decided in favour of those who wished to beautify their church services. The competition for the post of organist was held in August, and Herschel came through with flying colours in the face of stiff opposition. The story goes that with the help of two lead weights which he used to hold down an octave in the bass (English organs at that period were built without pedals) he improvised on this ground bass and produced such a massive volume of harmonious sonority that the judges were immediately convinced of his superiority over the other competitors, who had relied on ten fingers alone.

Just at this time Herschel received out of the blue an offer of the post of organist at the new Octagon Chapel at Bath. He must have felt that it never rains but it pours; but as the Octagon Chapel was not yet opened, nor its organ built, he decided to continue at Halifax for the time being, although he provisionally accepted the Bath engagement. In October he handed in his resignation at Halifax, and on 1st December 1766 he set out for London, *en route* for Bath, having played at Halifax on only thirteen Sundays—for which he received the sum of thirteen guineas.

Two terse but significant entries occur in his diary for this year: 'Feb. 19: Wheatley. Observation of Venus. Feb. 24: Eclipse of the moon at 7 o'clock A.M. Kirby.' These record naked-eye observations, perhaps made quite casually, but it is interesting that Herschel thought them worth mentioning in a diary whose entries sketch only the barest outline of his life at this period.

Certain passages in his correspondence with Jacob suggest that the satisfaction he derived from music as the mainspring of his life was lessening; and there is a brief note in his diary, made at the time of his removal to Halifax, which clearly indicates the direction of this reorientation: 'My leisure time was employed in reading mathematical books, such as the works of Emerson, Maclaurin, Hodgson, Smith's Harmonics, etc. This happened to be noticed by one of the Messrs. Bates [friends and patrons of Herschel in Halifax], who remarked to his brother: "Mr. Herschel reads Fluxions!"' Mathematics —to whose study Herschel was first led by a desire to improve his understanding of musical theory—was increasingly commanding his attention in its own right. And when, sixteen years later, he was to forsake music for good, and devote the whole of his time and his immense energies to astronomy, he could do so without a single recorded word of regret.

Born the son of Isaac Herschel, and inheriting from him a very considerable ability as an executant, William could hardly have adopted any other profession than music. But events proved that it was not the right choice. His true bent was scientific rather than artistic, and had he been born into a scientific instead of into a musical household there is little doubt that his life's work of scientific investigation and discovery would have started twenty years earlier than in fact it did.

William was an extremely talented performer: his versatility is shown by his performance at a benefit concert at the Bath Rooms soon after his arrival, when he, a professional organist, played 'a solo concert on the violin, one on the hautboy [oboe], and a sonata on the harpsichord'. But although he himself would have preferred to be a great composer rather than a virtuoso performer, his own compositions lack the mark of greatness. They are pleasant enough; he loved, and had the ability to construct, an agreeably flowing melodic line. But there was nothing of the fire and conviction of genius in Herschel's creative musical work, and we need not mourn the loss to posterity of another Mozart or Bach. It is, by the way, rather strange that a man with Herschel's particular cast of mind should have had little liking for the fugues of Bach (Handel was his idol and his pattern of excellence); for one of his most marked mental characteristics was a love of order, and a driving compulsion to classify and arrange the seeming motley of nature, introducing meaning and coherence where before there were none.

When Herschel arrived in Bath during the last days of 1766 he still had sixteen years as a practising musician ahead of him.

These were the culmination of the first period of his life; success, acclaim, and growing prosperity were his; the penniless music copier of nine years before was now a misty and unreal figure. William had established his roots in his new country; he was a public figure in a town which was then the centre of the fashionable world; his considerable personal charm, and the gaiety and friendliness of his disposition, assured him of all the social success he might want; he must have imagined that he had at last reached his goal. Yet he was at this time only approaching the portals of his true life's work, and from the organ loft at the Octagon Chapel he was to travel much further than the petty distance he had already covered—was to travel, indeed, into realms where no human mind had ever before penetrated.

CHAPTER THREE

ENTER CAROLINE

William entered upon his new life at Bath with enthusiasm and with his habitual energy. After a brief return visit to the north to tidy up his affairs there, he established himself at a house in Beauford Square and began looking for pupils. He also joined the 'established band of musicians'—the municipal orchestra that played regularly throughout the season at the Pump Room and Theatre, as well as at the frequent balls, routs, and ridottos which contributed to the gaiety of eighteenth-century Bath. He played both the violin and the oboe until disagreements with the director of the orchestra led him to resign. This director, incidentally, was the father of Elizabeth Linley, that beautiful and talented delight of the scandalmongers who sang the soprano solos at her father's concerts until her romantic elopement with the playwright Sheridan put an end to her career as a songstress.

William was also busily engaged during his first summer at Bath in forming and training a choir for the Octagon Chapel, and in composing anthems, hymn tunes and psalms of suitable simplicity for his inexperienced choristers. Private pupils, meanwhile, were increasingly occupying his time and attention. In November 1767 he noted in his diary that he had 'many scholars', and again in December that he was 'in full employment with public business and private scholars'. By 1772 the number of his private lessons had risen to thirty or forty a week, and at times he gave as many as seven in a single day.

The Bath Season lasted from October to Easter; during these winter months the fashionable world from London—and, indeed, the whole country—repaired to the mild West Country to take advantage of the waters, the balls, the gatherings at the Pump Room, the theatre and concerts, and above all the unparalleled opportunity to gossip, to consort with one's social equals or superiors, and to show off one's own elegance. During the summer, Bath was as much a city of the dead as a university town during vacation or, say, modern Blackpool in January. Many of William's pupils left Bath in the spring, when also the concerts were suspended and, probably, the Octagon Chapel closed. Herschel at these times resorted to his old routine of horseback travel, visiting pupils at country houses in the neighbourhood and at times going as far afield as Winchester and Salisbury to perform at concerts.

In the spring of 1767 his old friends the Bulmans joined him in Bath. Mr. Bulman's business had failed, and William had obtained for him the post of clerk to the Octagon Chapel. As before, the Bulmans and William Herschel settled down together, and Mrs. Bulman undertook the housekeeping for the joint household. In June Jacob arrived from Hanover on a visit which was to last two years. Meanwhile work on the chapel was being hurried on, for the official opening had been fixed for October—the season when Bath began to stir again after its summer sleep.

The Octagon Chapel was in its way a curious institution. It was a proprietary establishment, and the first of a number of such privately owned places of worship that sprang up in the town. They were much patronized by the fashionable visitors who thronged Bath during the Season, their popularity springing from their snobbish exclusiveness—for there the Quality could converse with their Maker without being forced into objectionable proximity with the lower orders whom they could not avoid during attendance at the Abbey. The Abbey, also, was cold and draughty, whereas at the Octagon Chapel six fires were kept going for the comfort of the worshippers. An advertisement in the local press, which appeared soon after the opening, gave warning that 'As this Chapel is private property and consequently no Persons can with any reason expect that the Sexton should open the pews to them unless they have taken seats, this public Notice is given that all Strangers who come to Bath for the Seasons, should apply to the Clerk. . .'

In October the chapel was formally opened. For the occasion an oratorio was performed: William led the instrumentalists as first violin and his brother Jacob played the organ.

The following summer William was joined by another member of the family. Isaac Herschel had died in March, soon after William had established himself at Bath, and on his deathbed he had placed the responsibility for Dietrich's musical education in Jacob's hands. (Dietrich, the youngest member of the family, was then twelve years old—sixteen years William's junior.) Jacob, who a few months later left Hanover to join William in Bath, therefore wrote to his mother asking that Dietrich be allowed to follow him to England. Anna Herschel was at first unwilling to let him go, since he had not yet been confirmed. But finally she agreed to Jacob's proposals, and in July 1768 Dietrich arrived at Beauford Square. He remained only a year, however, for when Anna learned that his religious instruction was being neglected and that he still had not been confirmed she insisted that he should return to Hanover. This he did in the company of Jacob during the summer of 1769.

William was not long to be without the companionship of his own family, however, for Jacob returned to Bath in 1770, and with him this time he brought Alexander, William's third brother, who was then a young man of twenty-five. Like his elder brothers, Alexander was a talented musician. During part of his youth he had lived with his eldest sister Sophia, who had married a musician named Griesbach, living at Coppenbrügge, not far from Hanover. It appears that Alexander was extremely unhappy in this household, for his brother-in-law was a harsh and intolerant taskmaster. Later, like Jacob before him, he joined the Court orchestra and returned to live at Hanover. There, perhaps in reaction from the privations and restrictions he had suffered at Coppenbrügge, he broke out into the wild ways of a gay young man about town. However understandable this may have been, neither his salary nor the financial position of the family was adequate to meet extravagances of this sort, and Caroline records in her memoirs: 'I was extremely discomposed to seeing Alex. associating with young men who led him into all manner of expensive pleasures which involved him in debts for the Hire of Horses, Carioles, etc., and I was (though he knew my inability to help him) made a partaker in his fears that these scrapes should come to the knowledge of our Mother.'

It is possible that William, hearing of Alexander's carryings on, was instrumental in bringing him to England. Jacob returned to Hanover soon afterward, and in 1792 died at the early age of fifty-eight. Alexander, however, made England his home; he began giving 'cello lessons and joined the Bath orchestra the year after his arrival, staying on in Bath when

William moved to Windsor some years later. There he remained until he finally returned to Hanover in 1816.

Two years after Alexander settled in Bath, William paid a short visit to Hanover. He travelled via Paris—where he visited the Opera and was 'much surprised to hear all the recitatives chanted like Cathedral music'—and Nancy, where he stayed with his Bath friends and original sponsors of the Octagon Chapel appointment, Dr. and Mrs. de Chair.

When he returned to England he brought Caroline with him.

Caroline, then a girl of twenty-two, was to play a central role in the unfolding of the Herschel story. Her life during the five years since her father's death had not been happy. She had been devoted to him, and was temperamentally much more akin to him than to her mother. Jacob she found ill-tempered, selfish and domineering: his view of his younger sister's job in life was that she should contribute to his own comfort, and nothing more. Anna Herschel, her mother, was likewise content to see Caroline degenerate into a domestic drudge. Anna was a typical *hausfrau*—religious, exclusively domestic in her interests, mystified by her husband's intellectual interests and quite intolerant of his efforts to stimulate the minds and widen the horizons of his children. She had never taken any part in the intellectual life of the household during Isaac's lifetime, having neither the mental equipment nor the desire to do so. As might be expected, she held that woman's proper place is the kitchen, and she had no patience at all with Caroline's deep-seated desire for self-improvement and the acquisition of some talent that would enable her to support herself. Caroline, who had inherited her full share of Isaac's mental alertness, must have found it a misery to have her life turned into a continuous round of chores.

Caroline's memoirs of this period of her life conjure up a picture of a forlorn and rather Cinderella-like figure, over-worked, under-appreciated and committed without hope of reprieve to the drudgery of the scullery. Her mother refused to allow her to take lessons in French, and when she wanted to attend Mme. Kuster's sewing classes Jacob only gave her permission to do so on the condition that she should confine her efforts to making clothes for him. It is hard to see in this pathetic figure the woman who was later to share in her brother's triumphs, to secure international recognition as an astronomer in her own right, and to be honoured by many of the scientific academies and learned societies of Europe.

Caroline had always felt for William an ardent affection and admiration: it is no uncommon thing for a young sister in a large family to select one of her elder brothers as an object of hero-worship, and William had from her earliest childhood always been her 'best and dearest of Brothers'. William, for his part, seems to have treated her with greater kindness and understanding than her other brothers or her elder sister. Many years later she still remembered how, when the Guards regiment returned from England, she (then a small girl of six) had missed her father at the parade, and had returned home, cold, lonely and tired, to find the family re-united round the dinner table—'nobody greeting me but my Brother William, who came running and crouched down to me, which made me forget all my grievances. I mention this instance of my Brother's attention as it was the last I should receive from him (though it was not the first) for years to come.' She also recalled her intense disappointment that on William's first visit after settling in England, she was unable to see as much of him as she wanted to, since she was then undergoing her final preparations for confirmation.

No doubt Alexander's descriptions of the Herschel household, and of Caroline's position in it, were at the back of William's determination to bring her to live with him in

Bath; certainly it was from Alexander that he learned that Caroline had a good voice. This led him to write to his mother suggesting that she should come to Bath for a two-years' trial, during which she could take singing lessons, with a view to becoming a professional singer. One can imagine Caroline's excitement on hearing of this proposal. She had always been consumed with a desire for independence, and William's letter must have brought a ray of hope into an existence that was unbearably stultifying and dull. Her hopes nevertheless looked like being dashed: Anna was openly scornful of the proposal; and Jacob frowned on a course of action that would deprive him of a hard-working and unpaid domestic slave. Despite the unfavourable reception of William's suggestion she did not lose heart, but began to prepare for the longed-for departure by practising singing whenever she had the house to herself (learning the solo parts of violin concertos, '*shake and all*', with a gag between her teeth), and by building up a stockpile of net ruffles and knitted stockings that would last Jacob, Dietrich and her mother for two years.

So things hung fire for a year or more, till William decided to force the issue by going to Hanover in person to fetch her. The last objections were overcome by his offer to contribute a yearly sum of money for a servant to replace Caroline, and from that time, 1772, till the day of his death fifty years later she was his constant companion—housekeeper, secretary, collaborator in his astronomical observations, and, to the end, utterly devoted assistant in all his work. She completely identified William's interests with her own, and for half a century served him with a self-disregarding devotion that puts one in mind of another remarkable sister whose brother likewise was William—Dorothy Wordsworth.

From 1772 onward we have more intimate knowledge of William Herschel's daily life, for his rather skeletal diary is now supplemented by Caroline's much more detailed memoirs. Their journey to England was eventful rather than pleasant. The packetboat ran into severe storms and came to port a semi-wreck, with her mainmast gone and her passengers much the worse for wear. Caroline was dumped unceremoniously onto English soil from the back of a sailor who had carried her ashore from a rowing boat. The next day the cart that had been hired to take them to meet the stage coach was overturned when the horse took fright and bolted, and poor Caroline was hurled into a ditch—fortunately with no worse damage than bruises. They spent one night in London, and eventually reached Bath eleven days after setting out from Hanover.

William had by now moved from Beauford Square into a house in New King Street. Alexander lived in one of the attics, Caroline was established in another, and the main part of the house was given over to William and the Bulmans. Caroline had little opportunity to get over the effects of her journey, for on the second day after her arrival William started her on English and arithmetic lessons, as well as introducing her to the intricacies of household book-keeping. William was up to his eyes in work, and Caroline saw little of him except at mealtimes; the 'Little Lessons for Lina', jotted down on odd scraps of paper, became an established feature of the Herschel breakfast table. Singing lessons, at the rate of two or even three a day, were also started immediately. When, later on, her English accent had improved sufficiently, she also attended the choir practices at the Octagon Chapel. All in all, it was a spartan régime of self-improvement upon which Caroline found herself embarked; there was possibly even less time for relaxation than there had been while she was drudging in Hanover. But there were two great differences between life in Germany and life in Bath, and these were more than enough to make the transition from the one to another almost an exchange of purgatory for paradise. She was with her beloved brother, cherished, loved and appreciated. And, at last, she was on the road to the realization of her old ambition to perfect herself in 'any branch of knowledge by which I could hope to gain a creditable livelihood'. Caroline, though frail and slight physically, was made of tough material; she was well equipped with fortitude and determination; born a century later she would probably have been a suffragette. As it was, she became one of the most remarkable women of her generation.

At first, it is true, the move from Hanover to Bath, which she had looked forward to with so much eagerness, brought disappointment: she suffered from homesickness, and her memoirs are full of regrets that she saw so little of the busily engaged William. But as her English improved and contact with those around her became easier to establish, her *heimwehe* faded away, though she never became reconciled to the artificiality of Bath society. 'Mrs. —— and her daughter were very civil,' she records of acquaintances made at that time, 'and the latter came sometimes to see me; but being more annoyed than entertained by her visits I did not encourage them, for I thought her little better than an idiot. The same opinion I had of Miss Bulman, for which reason I never could be sochiable with her.' These comments are typical. Serious-minded to a degree, Caroline could extract little pleasure from the fripperies and gigglings of gossiping young ladies; and being wholly lacking in the peculiarly artificial social graces which were *de rigueur* in the fashionable world of Bath, she in fact and quite simply felt at a hopeless disadvantage. Years later—writing a bread-and-butter letter to Maskelyne, the Astronomer Royal, in the involved style of English from which she never freed herself—she explained, 'I have too little knowledge of the rooles of Society as to trust much to my acquitting myself so as to give hope of having made any favourable impressions'. Even Mrs. Colbrooke—one of William's pupils, a rich widow who for a time had her matrimonial eye on him, and Caroline's host on a disastrous six-weeks' visit to London in 1774—was described as 'a wimsical Lady' who 'though learned and clever, was very capricious and ill-natured'.

If Caroline was to shine at all, it had to be in the company of a small circle of well-known and well-loved friends: her own dry and unemphatic brand of humour—often seen in her letters, less frequently in her memoirs—then had a chance to display itself. A nice example of this wit, no less caustic for being subdued, occurs in a letter she wrote to Maskelyne on another occasion: having admitted that her vanity had been pleasantly tickled by a compliment he had paid to her work, she continued, 'You see, Sir, I do own myself to be vain because I would not wish to be singular, and was there ever a woman without vanity?—or a man either?—only with this difference, that among gentlemen the comodity is generally stiled ambition'.

Coping with a succession of dirty and dishonest servants (Caroline always distrusted servants, and probably brought out the worst in them), keeping the household books, taking lessons in English cookery from Mrs. Bulman,[1] doing the shopping and marketing—to all this were added her musical and educational occupations. 'One of the principal things required was to market', she records, with the sort of humorous desperation that had its basis in fact, 'and about six weeks after

[1] 'The first hours immediately after breakfast were spent in the Kittschen, where Mrs. Bulman taught me to make all sorts of Pudings and Piys, besides many things in the Confectionary business, Pickling and preserving, &c., &c., a knowledge for which it was not likely I should ever have occasion.'

coming to England I was sent alone among fishwomen, butchers, basket-women, etc., and I brought home whatever in my fright I could pick up. . . . But all attempts to introduce any order in our little household proved vain, owing to the servant my Brother then had—a hot-headed old Welsh-woman. All the articles, tea-things, etc., which I was to take in charge, were almost all destroyed: knives eaten up by rust, heaters of the tea-urn found in the ash-hole, etc. And what still further increased my difficulty was, that my Brother's time was entirely taken up with business, so that I only saw him at meals. Breakfast was at 7 o'clock or before (much too early for me),—who would rather have remained up all night than be obliged to rise at so early an hour.' Had she but known it, she was to have more than ample opportunity to stay up entire nights during the years to come.

But despite all the hindrances and distractions to which she was subjected she made good progress with her singing, and fully justified Alexander's opinion of her voice. Following in the footsteps of the dazzling Elizabeth Linley, who had captivated Bath as well by her voice as her beauty, Caroline had no enviable task in establishing herself as a singer. For a year she took two lessons a week from a Miss Fleming, whom she described as 'the celebrated dantzing Mistress', to fit her for her public appearances. By 1777 she was singing solo parts in oratorios such as *The Messiah* and *Judas Maccabaeus*, and taking part in as many as five performances a week at both Bristol and Bath. She was first singer at the Winter Concerts of 1778, and in the same year received an offer of an engagement to sing at Birmingham; but this she declined, since she was unwilling to sing when her brother was not conducting.

Nevertheless, Caroline was destined for another career than that of professional singer. With each succeeding year William was more heavily engaged with his private pupils and his public duties. In 1776 he was appointed director of the Bath orchestra in succession to Linley—who had departed for London to take over Drury Lane Theatre in partnership with his son-in-law Sheridan. William, moreover, was becoming more and more preoccupied with science. (He had, at this time, started building his own telescopes.) The increasing demands made on Caroline's time and energies as a result of all this—and the Bulmans' return to Leeds in 1775 had transferred all the housekeeping to her shoulders—forced her little by little to relinquish her musical ambitions. To what extent she regretted this final stultification of her most cherished hopes, once so bright, it is impossible to discern in her memoirs, which are strangely colourless and unrevealing where her own feelings are concerned. But even though she may have been saddened by the collapse of her musical career—and it is difficult to suppose that she was not—the years ahead held rewards in store for her that amply justified her sacrifice.

CHAPTER FOUR

MUSIC AND ASTRONOMY

During his first five years at Bath William seems to have been occupied with music and his professional work to the exclusion of all else. His position in the Bath orchestra, his own choir at the Octagon Chapel—which he had not only to train but also to keep supplied with suitable music—and his private pupils, who by 1771 were sometimes coming at the rate of seven a day—all this, in accelerating tempo, prevented him from developing further those intellectual interests of which many entries in his Yorkshire diary and his letters to Jacob bear witness. He was no doubt still reading in optics and astronomy, or at least giving a passing thought to his old loves, but there is no documentary evidence of this: his diary, always brief to vanishing point, is limited to notes of musical events, the comings and goings of his brothers, the rents of his houses, and his steadily growing annual income.

Then, quite suddenly, comes the change. The last two notes in his diary for the year 1772, which are typical of those that have gone before, read:

Aug. 27. Arrived at Bath [i.e. on his return from Hanover with Caroline].

Sept. 1 Began again to teach my resident scholars. Following this, like the eruption of an obsession that has been too long suppressed and denied expression, is a series of entries of a totally different character.

1773

April 19. Bought a quadrant and Emerson's Trigonometry.

May 10. Bought a book of astronomy and one of astronomical tables.

May 24. Bought an object glass of 10 feet focal length.

June 1. Bought many eye glasses, and tin tubes made.

June 7. Glasses paid for and the use of a small reflector paid for.

June 14. Boxes for glasses paid for. The hire of a 2 feet reflecting telescope for 3 months paid for.

June 21 to Aug. 23. Many glasses, tubes.

Sept. 15. Hired a 2 feet reflector.

Sept. 22. Bought tools for making a reflector. Had a metal cast.

Oct. 2. Bought a 20 feet object glass and nine eye-glasses, etc. Emerson's Optics. Attended private scholars as usual.

Nov. 8. Attended 40 scholars this week. Public business as usual.

Nov. 15. Attended 46 private scholars; nearly 8 per day.

This is the longest year's entry in William's diary since his arrival in Bath. The relative importance and interest of music and astronomy in his eyes speaks clearly from this extract. The terse, casual notes on his pupils and his public work towards the end of the year give the impression of being there only on sufferance, and as a sort of absent-minded afterthought.

Why his long-incubated interest in astronomy should have burst forth with such intensity at this particular juncture it is impossible to say with certainty. It was clearly not that he had more time to devote to it, for each succeeding year at Bath saw him increasingly in demand as a music teacher and performer. Perhaps the breach in his routine occasioned by his visit to Paris and Hanover was the immediate cause. For several years the importunate demands of his day-to-day duties had kept his nose so close to the grindstone that he had had no opportunity to pause for breath, to look around, or take any sort of mental stock.

Two small incidents of his holiday away from Bath during the summer of 1772 hint at the imminent resurgence of his interest in astronomy—an interest that had been lying dormant beneath the surface of his musical commitments and activities. Caroline, after describing in her memoirs the routine of life into which she settled on her arrival in Bath, adds: 'By way of relaxation we talked of astronomy and the bright constellations with which I had made acquaintance during the fine nights we spent on the Postwagen travelling through Holland.' It is evident that William had spent part of those nights of travel pointing out to her and naming the constellations spread out above the wide Dutch horizons.

Again, Caroline's description of their overnight stay in London includes the illuminating recollection that 'in the evening, when the shops were lighted up, we went to see all that was to be seen in that part of London; of which I only remember the optician shops, for I do not think we stopt at any other.'

During these two years, 1772 and 1773, the underlying pattern of William's life began, as it were, to gel. The outward circumstances of his first thirty-five years may appear to be eventful, changeful and disjointed. But beneath them the man

Caroline Herschel in her old age

who William was by virtue of his heredity and his early training was developing steadily. And this man was not a violinist or choirmaster, still less a composer, but a scientist—a lover of impersonal knowledge, and above all a man possessed of the divine inquisitiveness of the born research worker. He was designed by nature to be a discoverer, an explorer not of the Earth's surface but of the infinitely vaster expanse of the visible Universe. Circumstances had long hindered the manifestation of his true bent, but its development from his earliest years had been continuous and, in its inner logic, inevitable. Now that development could no longer be denied expression

The story of that crucial year 1773, whose bare bones we have seen in William's diary, is filled out in greater detail by Caroline. After describing the homesickness and loneliness of her first winter in England, and her hope that with the ending of the Season she would see more of her brother, she continues: 'But I was greatly disappointed; for, in consequence of the harassing and fatiguing life he had led during the winter months, he used to retire to bed with a bason of milk or glass of water, and Smith's *Harmonics* and *Optics*, Ferguson's *Astronomy*, etc., and so went to sleep buried under his favourite authors; and his first thoughts on rising were how to obtain instruments for viewing those objects himself of which he had been reading.'

To appreciate Herschel's immense achievements as a telescope builder, it will be necessary to digress for a moment into the field of practical optics. Telescopes are of two main types, refractors and reflectors. The former, as their name implies, make use of the ability of glass to refract or bend a ray of light passing through it. This bending occurs whenever light passes from one medium, such as air, into another medium of different density, such as water or glass. (The apparent bending of a straight stick held half in and half out of water is a familiar example.) It is by virtue of refraction that a convex lens can form an image of a distant object. When a lens is used as a burning glass, for example, the brilliant spot of light that can be seen on the surface of the paper before it bursts into flame is in fact a tiny image of the Sun. Such an image, however, is too small to be observed effectively—it needs to be magnified. A refracting telescope is, in essence, simply an instrument which supplies a magnifying glass for the examination of the image formed by the object glass. This magnifying glass is called the ocular or eyepiece, and nowadays usually consists not of a single lens but of a combination of two or more lenses, though Herschel commonly used single-lens eyepieces in his telescopes.

The distance from the object glass—the large lens at the 'top' of the telescope—to the image which it forms of any very distant object such as the Moon, is called its focal length. A rack adjustment allows the telescope to be 'focused' by moving the eyepiece in or out, nearer to or further from the object glass. When the eye lens lies at a distance behind the primary image which is equal to its own focal length, the image will be seen in focus, magnified, and apparently as far away as the object itself. The amount of the magnification depends solely upon the relative focal lengths of the objective and the eyepiece. If the focal length of the objective is 60 ins. and that of the eyepiece 1 in., then the telescope will magnify 60 times. The magnification of a telescope (which is simply the focal length of the object glass divided by that of the eyepiece) can thus be varied at will by using eyepieces of different focal lengths—the shorter the focal length of the ocular the higher the magnification, and vice versa.

The principle of the refracting telescope had been discovered accidentally in the early years of the seventeenth century by a Dutch spectacle-maker named Lippershey. The story goes that he happened one day to look at the spire of a distant church through two lenses which he was holding up in line, one behind the other. By a lucky chance the distance separating the lenses must have been just right (the sum of their focal lengths) because to his amazement he found that the spire appeared to have been brought quite close to him. Within a few years Galileo had heard accounts of this epoch-making discovery, and with primitive little instruments of his own making had become the first telescopic astronomer: he discovered the mountains on the Moon, four of the moons that revolve round the planet Jupiter, and the fact that the pearly light of the Milky Way is made up of myriads of stars which are too faint to be seen individually by the naked eye.[1]

For small spy-glasses such an optical arrangement is satisfactory enough, but a simple convex lens is by no means a perfect image-former—as the seventeenth-century telescopists soon discovered. The chief defect from which a lens of this sort suffers is that known as chromatic aberration. The action of a glass prism in splitting up a beam of white light into its constituent colours is familiar to everyone. This splitting-up action relies on the fact that the prism is refracting light of different colours by different amounts. Now a simple lens may be regarded as a prism with curved sides. Thus it does not simply bend the light from, say, a star so that it converges to form a single image of the star: it bends the constituent colours by different amounts (depending on their wavelength), bringing each to a focus at a slightly different distance from itself. It follows that no one position of the eyepiece will show a sharply

[1] The discovery of sunspots is usually, though incorrectly, attributed to Galileo also. In fact, the earliest recorded observation of them was made by Thomas Harriot, who had had specimens of the new invention sent over from Holland and had then immediately set to work grinding his own lenses. He was the first English telescopist.

focused image of all the light from the star that is passing through the object glass: it may be adjusted to the focus of the yellow light, but then the sharply defined yellow image of the star will be surrounded by spurious colour due to the slightly out-of-focus blue, red, and other coloured images.

The early telescopists discovered that the objectionable effects of chromatic aberration could be reduced (though not eliminated) by making the focal length of the object glass very great compared with its diameter. This led to the building of the enormously elongated telescopes of the seventeenth century, whose apertures (as the clear diameter of the objective is termed) still remained comparatively small. This was a severe limitation on the development of the refractor, for, as we shall see later, a telescope is not *only* a magnifying instrument, and its other and equally important functions require a large aperture, not long focal length. On purely practical grounds, too, the usefulness of these great spindly telescopes, sometimes as long as 400 feet, was very restricted: with the primitive mountings then in use—the unwieldy tube was usually slung by ropes from a tall pole—the telescope could not be quickly and easily directed to any part of the sky, while on any but the most windless night its unsteadiness rendered it unusable: as well try to keep a telescope trained steadily on a distant and tiny object while riding pillion on a motor bicycle over a cobbled street.

Very early in its history, then, the refractor ran into difficulties that at the time seemed to present an insuperable barrier to its development into a powerful scientific instrument. Two avenues of escape from this impasse were eventually found, the earlier of which was the invention of the reflecting telescope by James Gregory in 1663; the first telescope actually to be constructed on this principle, some five years later, was the work of no less a personage than Newton himself.

Gregory proposed to by-pass chromatic aberration by making use of reflection, instead of refraction, in the formation of the telescopic image. For although light of different colours is unequally refracted, all wavelengths are reflected together through exactly the same angle: there is therefore no prism-action, no spectrum-formation, when light is reflected from a smooth, polished surface. Gregory therefore proposed that the telescopic objective should not be a lens *through* which the light is refracted, but a concave mirror *from* which it is reflected. For a concave mirror (such as a shaving mirror, for example) is just as capable as a convex lens of forming an image.

The design of the two types of telescope is of course quite different. The reflector's objective—the concave mirror—lies at the bottom of the tube, the upper end of which (where the object glass would be in a refractor) is open. Light from a star passes down the tube, is reflected from the mirror, returns up the tube as a converging beam to form an image at the focus near the upper end of the tube. But if the mirror is set absolutely square in the tube, this image will be formed in the centre of the tube, where it will be impossible to see without the observer's head getting in the way of the incoming light. In the reflector that Newton designed and made, a small flat mirror was mounted centrally just inside the mouth of the tube and inclined at 45° to the tube's axis. The converging beam from the objective was intercepted by this 'flat' and reflected through a hole in the side of the tube to the eyepiece. When using a Newtonian reflector, therefore, the observer stands sideways-on to the object whose image he is looking at.[1]

[1] In Gregory's original design the small mirror was not an inclined 'flat' but another concave mirror, facing down the tube; the beam converging from it passed to the eyepiece through a hole in the centre of the objective. A more useful modification, suggested by Cassegrain and still extensively used, differs from the Gregorian only in having a convex secondary mirror. With both these types of reflector (as with the refractor), the observer faces towards the object he is looking at.

By the time that William Herschel was turning his attention to telescope building, rather more than a century later, the second way of defeating chromatic aberration had recently been discovered; this method retained refraction as the means of forming the image. In 1758, William's first year in London, an optician named Dollond had discovered a way of making a compound lens with greatly reduced chromatic aberration. This so-called achromatic lens consisted of two components, one convex and the other concave, made of different kinds of glass. By selecting crown and flint glass of just the right densities for the two components he was able to retain the image-forming action of the combination (i.e. the two components together were effectively a convex lens) while their aberrations largely cancelled one another out.

It would seem that Herschel was not aware of Dollond's discovery, for it was partly because of the great tube lengths of his few trial refractors that he abandoned them in favour of reflectors. Another reason was that it was possible to make much larger mirrors than lenses. Thereafter he remained faithful to the reflector all his life, and carried the development and construction of this type of telescope to hitherto undreamed of lengths. For many years his greatest instrument—40 feet focal length, with a mirror 4 feet in diameter—was the largest in existence, a recognized showpiece for sightseers and visitors to England, and the talk of the scientific world.

Let us now return to William, at the close of the Bath Season in the spring of 1773. The books which had so absorbed him during the winter months that he would fall asleep at night 'buried under them', had kindled into incandescence the spasmodic interest in astronomy that he had shown all his life. He was no longer content merely to read descriptions of the wonders hidden in the depths of the night sky—he must see them for himself. And when the conclusion of the Season released him from some of the musical engagements that occupied his time so fully during the winter, he set about realising that ambition. As we have seen, he wasted no time, for the entry in his diary of May 24th reads 'Bought an object glass of 10 feet focal length'—nine words that record the turning point of his life.

His first telescopes were refractors: a 4-foot,[1] magnifying about 40 times, with which he made his first telescopic observations of the planets and stars; this was followed in rapid succession by a 12-foot, a 15-foot, and finally a 30-foot refractor. The problem of efficiently mounting such long tubes was largely responsible for turning his attention to reflectors, and by September he had hired a Gregorian reflector of 2 feet focal length. This he found such a luxury to use, after the unmanageable refractors, that he made inquiries regarding the possibility of purchasing larger mirrors that he himself could mount. But when he learnt that they would have to be specially made for him, at a cost that was beyond the reach of his pocket, his thoughts turned to the possibility of grinding and polishing his own mirrors. As yet he had undertaken no optical work—the 2-foot reflector was a hired instrument, and he had himself only assembled the refractors, whose lenses had been purchased ready made. So, 'I soon resolved to try whether I could not make myself such another [as his little Gregorian], with the assistance of Dr. Smith's popular treatise on Optics.'

Just about this time he had the good fortune to hear of a resident of Bath, a Quaker, who had made a hobby of grinding and polishing mirrors for telescopes; this man had given up his optical work, and William bought all his tools and workshop equipment, as well as some half-finished mirrors.

[1] Throughout this book, when a *telescope* is described in this way, it is the focal length of the objective that is referred to; when an *objective* (mirror or object glass) is described as, for instance, a 4-foot, this is its diameter, or aperture.

Modern telescope mirrors are made from glass discs, on whose concave upper surface a film of silver or aluminium is deposited. But in Herschel's day the technique of depositing metallic silver on glass was unknown, and mirrors were made of polished speculum metal—an alloy of tin and copper. Having bought his second-hand equipment, William immediately ordered the casting of two discs of speculum metal which he intended for mirrors of 2 feet focal length—the grinding, figuring and polishing to be undertaken by hand himself. In November he ordered other mirrors to be cast, one of which was to be for a 5½-foot telescope, and from this time onward the household at 7 New King Street became increasingly and chaotically involved in the work to which William was applying himself with a truly ferocious energy and tenacity. Both Alexander and Caroline found themselves pressed into service. Alexander, who had some of his brother's mechanical skill, was always glad enough to lend a hand when some interesting piece of gadgetry was afoot, though the long and tedious hours of grinding the mirrors were for William alone. Caroline took less kindly than Alexander to the upheaval of her domestic organization and to the messy jobs she was asked to undertake in the workshop. William's sudden emergence as a practical optician sounded the death knell of her musical career, for although she still managed to continue her singing for a number of years, it was as William's assistant, secretary and universal helpmeet that she was increasingly heavily engaged.

Some of the passages in her memoirs bring this strange household vividly before our eyes. 'I was much hindered in my musical practice by my help being continually wanted in the execution of the various contrivances, and I had to amuse myself with making the tube of pasteboard for the glasses which were to arrive from London, for at that time no optician had settled in Bath. But when all was finished, no one besides my

Brother could get a glimpse of Jupiter or Saturn, for the great length of the tube would not allow it to be kept in a straight line. This difficulty, however, was soon removed by substituting tin tubes. . . . But nothing serious could be attempted, for want of time, till the beginning of June, when some of my Brother's scholars were leaving Bath; and then to my sorrow I saw almost every room turned into a workshop. A cabinet-maker making a tube and stands of all descriptions in a handsomely furnished drawing-room; Alex putting up a huge turning machine . . . in a bedroom, for turning patterns, grinding lenses, and turning eyepieces, etc. At the same time music durst not lie entirely dormant during the summer. . . . But every leisure moment was eagerly snatched at for resuming some work which was in progress, without taking time for changing dress, and many a lace ruffle (which were then worn) was torn or bespattered by molten pitch, etc.; besides the danger to which he continually exposed himself by this uncommon precipitancy which accompanied all his actions; of which we had a melancholy sample one Saturday when both Brothers returned from a Concert between 11 and 12 o'clock . . . and recollecting that the tools wanted sharpening, they ran with the Lanthorn and tools to our Landlord's grinding stone in a public yard. . . . But they had hardly gone when my Brother William was brought back fainting by Alex. with the loss of the nail of one of his fingers. . . . My time was so much taken up with copying Music and practising, besides attendance on my Brother when polishing, that by way of keeping him alife I was even obliged to feed him by putting the Vitals by bits into his mouth;—this was once the case when at the finishing of a 7-feet mirror he had not left his hands from it for 16 hours together. And in general he was never unemployed at meals, but always at the same time contriving or making drawings of whatever came into his mind. And generally I was obliged to read to him when at some work which required no thinking[1] and sometimes lending a hand, I became in time as useful a member of the workshop as a boy might be to his master in the first year of his apprenticeship.'

Early in 1774 the polish of the 5½-foot mirror was far enough advanced for it to be mounted and tried out. But William found that with the Gregorian arrangement the adjustment of the two mirrors was awkward and difficult, and he therefore adapted it as a Newtonian. This proved to be much more satisfactory, and on 1st March 1774 his astronomical journal opens with the record of observations of Saturn's rings and of the 'lucid spot in Orion's sword belt'.[2] His success with the 5½-foot was encouraging rather than satisfying, however, and he at once embarked on the construction of a 7-foot Newtonian.

William's tenacity, his indomitable energy in surmounting one obstacle after another, and his capacity for biting off much more than most men would be prepared to chew, were almost unbelievable. He had to teach himself the extremely difficult art of the optician as he went along, learning through an endless succession of errors made and corrected (helped only by a single textbook on optics and the few hints he had picked up from the Quaker—which had not amounted to much, 'his knowledge being very confined'); he had to experiment with different strokes of the mirror over the grinding tool, learning by trial and error the different effect of each upon the figure of the mirror's concave surface; he had to make trials of different forms of telescope construction; he had to design and make his own tubes, mounting and eyepieces. And all this was carried on in the hours left over from his musical duties.

From time to time, indeed, astronomy and music seem to

[1] *Don Quixote*, the *Arabian Nights*, and the works of Sterne and Fielding were among William's favourites.

[2] The great nebula in Orion, visible to the naked eye.

have become somewhat entangled—to the confusion and surprise of his pupils—as when in the middle of one lesson William noticed that the sky had cleared, and immediately dropped his violin and rushed to his telescope where he welcomed some star or other with crows of delight as a long-lost friend. William soon earned a local reputation as a star-gazer, and not infrequently he found that the pupils themselves were willing to turn what started as a violin lesson into a discussion on astronomy.

In the summer of 1774 the Herschels and Bulmans moved to a new house, near the Walcot turnpike on the outskirts of the town. This was better suited to the requirements of a combined musician-astronomer-telescope builder, since it had more space for workshops and there was a flat roof as well as a garden where telescopes could be set up. In the following year the Bulmans left—possibly they were less adaptable than Caroline in coping with the domestic upheavals occasioned by William's new activities—and Caroline recorded, rather forlornly, that 'during this summer I lost the only female acquaintances (not friends) I ever had the opportunity of being intimate with'. On the other hand it is clear that she regarded the daughter as a feather-brained moron, and had never taken to the elder Bulmans, so we cannot suppose that their going caused her much heartbreak.

On the resignation of Linley, the director of the Bath orchestra, William was offered the post; this he accepted, adding still further to the congestion of his affairs. He had by then completed a 10-foot in addition to the first 7-foot, and by July 1776 was making observations with a 20-foot which was mounted in the garden of the Walcot house. For each new telescope he made not one but several mirrors, finally selecting the best of them. His output of mirrors (each the result of many hours of grinding and polishing) would alone have been incredible, even if he had done no other work; in 1795 he wrote that he had by that time completed not less than 200 mirrors of 7 feet focal length, 150 of 10 feet, and about 80 of 20 feet.

There were two motives behind Herschel's demand for larger and larger telescopes. The first, and less important, concerns magnification: we have seen that a telescope of 10 feet focal length will give double the magnification of a 5-foot telescope using the same eyepiece, irrespective of the diameters of the two objectives. The second motive concerns what is known as light grasp. The brightness of the telescopic image of, say, a star depends upon the area of the objective (mirror or object glass) which is collecting the light that goes to form the image. Doubling the diameter of the objective increases its area four times: hence a 12-inch mirror will show stars that are four times as faint as the faintest that can be seen with a 6-inch mirror. There is an obvious connection between this and the distance into space that a telescope can penetrate. Doubling the distance of a star reduces its brightness four times; doubling the diameter of an objective increases the brightness of its images four times; hence doubling the diameter of an objective doubles its space penetration. This was clearly realized by Herschel, who was the first man to state explicitly the relation between aperture, light grasp, and space penetration.[1] And it was primarily this second reason—that large apertures reveal fainter and more distant objects than small apertures—that drove him with such dogged determination along the arduous path of constructing larger and larger telescopes.

While at Walcot, Herschel made some trials of a new form of telescope construction which, though they were not immediately followed up, led to the adoption of the 'front view' arrangement (now called the Herschelian) in all his later instruments. In the Gregorian and Newtonian forms, the specu-

[1] In his paper *On the Power of Penetrating into Space by Telescopes*, 1799.

lum is set square in the tube, with the result that the image is formed in an inaccessible position and a secondary mirror has to be used to reflect it to the eyepiece. This second reflection results in loss of light, since no mirror (and particularly a comparatively poor reflector such as speculum metal) reflects 100 per cent of the light falling on it. Herschel therefore had the idea of tilting the main mirror slightly, so that it reflected the converging cone of rays straight to an eyepiece mounted on the upper lip of the tube without the intervention of a secondary mirror. With a 'front view' instrument the observer thus stands with his back to the object he is observing.[1]

The routine of life at Bath was rudely interrupted in the summer of 1777 by the arrival of a letter from Anna Herschel announcing that Dietrich, accompanied by a young friend of his, had run away from home with the intention of sailing for the East Indies. William immediately posted to London, where he learnt that no boats were sailing to the Indies before December at the earliest. Confident, therefore, of catching up with Dietrich before he had an opportunity to leave Europe, William crossed to Holland where he instituted inquiries in Amsterdam and Rotterdam. These being fruitless he supposed that Dietrich had tired of his escapade and had returned home, and he himself went on to Hanover. Although there was no sign of Dietrich there, his companion turned up shortly afterward with the news that Dietrich had stayed on in Amsterdam and was intending to sail for London. William's quest seemed to be over, for he assumed that by now Dietrich would be safely in Caroline's care at Bath, and he therefore stayed on with his

[1] The Herschelian form of telescope has nowadays fallen into disuse since the tilting of the objective introduces the type of image distortion known as astigmatism. In Herschel's telescopes of this type, however, the ratio of focal length to aperture was so large that the ill effects of tilting the mirror were negligible.

mother for several weeks. Dietrich did not appear at Bath, however, and the first news that Caroline had of him was a letter from Wapping saying that he was lying very ill at an inn there, unable to travel further. Alexander in turn dropped all his engagements in Bath and went to London. There he saw that Dietrich had proper medical attention, and after a fortnight he was well enough to travel by easy stages to Bath, where William found him recuperating (on Caroline's rather Edward Learish diet of baked apples and barley water) when he returned from Hanover in late August or early September.

Soon after these events the Herschels moved back into Bath, for the Walcot house proved to be inconveniently remote from the town centre where much of William's musical work lay. Their new house, in New King Street again, had all the advantages of the Walcot turnpike house—sheds providing plenty of room for workshops, a garden where telescopes could be set up, and an uninterrupted view of the sky—with the added benefit of its central situation. Here Dietrich remained with his brother and sister (Alexander was now living on his own). William had arranged musical engagements for Dietrich without difficulty, for like all the rest of the family he had considerable talent. After staying for two years, he returned to Hanover in the summer of 1779, where he settled down and soon afterwards married. And so he passed out of William's life for many years, apart from the affectionate correspondence that continued between them.

CHAPTER FIVE

URANUS

The year 1779, when Dietrich was living with William and Caroline, was largely devoted to intensive experiments in the art and craft of speculum grinding. William had a supremely practical knack (the workshop equivalent of a gardener's green fingers) and a limitless fund of mechanical ingenuity. His optics, too, were of a practical rather than a theoretical nature. As he polished his mirrors he tested them out in a telescope, and if they gave good images of the stars he was satisfied, whether their figure was paraboloid, hyperboloid or whatever. The theoretically perfect figure for the reflecting surface is a paraboloid, and modern mirrors are worked to within a few millionths of an inch of this curve. In practice the disc is first ground with successive grades of carborundum to a perfect spherical curve; then, by the use of a different type of grinding stroke, the centre is further deepened very slightly, converting the surface from a sphere to a paraboloid; this extremely delicate operation, known as figuring, is followed by the final polishing.

That many of William Herschel's mirrors fell far short of the standard of accuracy achieved to-day mattered not a scrap: he tested them, not on an optical bench, but in the telescope, and he continued working on them until they gave satisfactory results with the actual eyepieces which were to be employed with them for astronomical observation.

Observations of planets are recorded in William's astronomical register for 1779, and it is probable that at about this time he was engaged with his first 'review of the heavens', which he undertook with the 7-foot Newtonian, magnifying 222 times, and with which he scrutinized every star in the heavens down to the fourth magnitude. His thoughts were also turning to a problem that in one form or another was to engage him till the end of his life, and from which sprang his earliest major additions to the store of astronomical knowledge. This was the problem of the distances of the stars. A few attempts at measuring the distance of a star had been made before William's time, but these had all been fruitless, and success only came finally in 1836, fourteen years after his death.

The basic principle of the measurement of a star's distance is easy enough to understand; it is the practical application of this principle that is so difficult, and demands highly refined instruments. If you are sitting in front of a window and look at the landscape outside, using first the right eye and then the left in rapid succession, you will notice that the window-pane appears to jerk backwards and forwards across the more distant background. This apparent movement, or parallax, of course arises from the fact that your eyes are about two inches apart, and that in using first one and then the other you are employing slightly different viewpoints.

The same principle can be used to determine the distances of the nearer heavenly bodies. When the position of the Moon, relative to the background of the vastly more distant stars, is measured simultaneously from two observatories several thousand miles apart, its parallax is large enough to be measured quite easily. But the more distant an object is, the smaller is its parallax for a given shift of viewpoint—the window experiment will show a parallax for the pane itself, but not for a tree at the bottom of the garden: to make the tree shift its apparent position against the horizon you will have to move your head bodily, or perhaps even walk to the other side of the room. In the same way, even the nearest stars are so enormously distant that no baseline on the Earth's surface is large enough to reveal any parallax; the Earth's surface is not large enough to provide two viewpoints that are sufficiently far apart.

But every year the Earth travels round the Sun in an orbit whose diameter is 186,000,000 miles. Thus on January 1st and June 1st, for instance, it is at opposite points in this orbit, and the two positions are nearly two hundred million miles apart. If we were to observe one of the nearest stars, measuring very carefully its position relative to its neighbours in the sky (some at least of which would be likely to be much more distant), then surely in six months' time, when we should be observing it from the other end of this immense baseline, some change in its apparent position would be noticed? All efforts to detect such an effect had, however, proved unsuccessful in Herschel's time. The practical difficulty is the detection of such a tiny displacement between the 'near' star and the more distant background stars. Herschel saw that the closer together in the sky, or in the telescopic field, the 'near' star and the comparison stars are, the easier would be the detection of any relative shift, During his long hours of observation when he had been reviewing the face of the night sky with his first telescopes, he had come across numerous double stars: these are stars which appear single to the naked eye, but which the telescope shows to consist of two stars, lying so close together that the naked eye cannot separate them. Frequently the two members of such pairs are of very unequal brightness. Now if, Herschel argued, we may say that *in general* a faint star is more distant than a bright one (and it seemed a safe enough generalization to make), then some of these doubles must consist of a star comparatively near to the Earth and one which happens to lie near the same line of sight but at a vastly greater distance. And because of their nearness to one another in the telescopic field, the parallax of the brighter should be easy to spot. From this purely theoretical interest in double stars sprang his pioneering researches in this field of astronomy.

The year 1778 also saw the completion of a 'most capital' mirror of 7 feet focal length, which became one of Herschel's favourite instruments; with it, three years later, he discovered the planet Uranus. In 1779 William again moved house—this time to No. 5 River Street. The motive for the move is rather puzzling; the new house was in many ways less convenient, and had no garden from which observations could be made. William was compelled to hire a garden elsewhere, in which to set up his 20-foot reflector, and was wont to make observations with his smaller and more portable instruments on the pavement outside his front door—a circumstance that was to have important consequences for him, as we shall see.

In August he began his second review of the heavens—an ambitious undertaking which entailed the examination of every star recorded on the star maps of Harris, together with its neighbours down to the eighth magnitude. The main purpose of the survey was the discovery of double stars that would be suitable for parallax determinations.

A word should perhaps be said here regarding the astronomer's method of grading the brightness of stars. The unit employed is the 'magnitude' and it is important to realize that this is simply the unit of apparent brightness, and has nothing whatever to do with the size of the star. Roughly speaking, the brightest stars in the sky are of the first magnitude, while the faintest that can be seen with the naked eye are of the sixth. A star of exactly the first magnitude (mag. 1·0) is 2·5 times brighter than a star whose magnitude is 2·0, and so on from magnitude to magnitude down the scale. An easy calculation will show, therefore, that a star of magnitude one is 100 times brighter than a star of magnitude six.

Herschel's second review of the heavens was made with his particularly excellent 7-foot reflector (the aperture of whose mirror was 6·2 inches), using an eyepiece which gave a magnification of 227 times.[1] The review took two years to complete, and its results included his first *Catalogue of Double Stars* (numbering 269), and the discovery of Uranus.

Herschel was also at this time giving a great deal of attention to the Moon, having embarked on a programme of measuring the heights of its mountains. This work led to a meeting which was to have important repercussions in his life. One night, late in December 1779, he was observing the Moon with his 7-foot telescope, which was set up in the street outside his house—as was his custom when the work in hand did not require the use of the 20-foot. A passer-by stopped to watch, and William gladly granted his request to look through the telescope. The stranger 'expressed great satisfaction at the view', and next morning presented himself at 19 New King Street to thank Herschel for his courtesy, and to introduce himself. He was Dr. Watson, later Sir William Watson, a Fellow of the Royal Society, who was to become William's lifelong friend and invaluable supporter. The immediate result of their meeting was that William became a member of the Bath Literary and Philosophical Society, of which Dr. Watson was also a member. Between January 1780 and March 1781 Herschel submitted no fewer than thirty-one papers to this society, and it is

[1] From what has already been said about the magnification of a telescope it can easily be calculated that the focal length of this eyepiece was a little more than one-third of an inch.

interesting to notice how his extraordinary versatility and the wide range of his interests are reflected in the subjects of these early papers. Astronomy is represented by three papers on the lunar mountains, two on the variable stars Mira (which William had begun observing in 1777), one on an occultation of the star gamma Virginis by the Moon (observed to see whether any effect attributable to a lunar atmosphere could be detected) and the now famous *Account of a Comet*, of which more will be said later. In addition there are papers dealing with natural history (experiments on the rate of growth of Corallines), physics (electricity and heat), optics (theoretical and lens-making), and with such philosophical themes as *On the Utility of Speculative Enquiries*, *On the Existence of Space*, and *On Liberty and Necessity*.

Herschel's meeting with Dr. Watson was instrumental in introducing him to the society of men of science—a world from which up to this time he had been entirely cut off. He was well known and highly esteemed in Bath as a musician, but his optical and astronomical work had been regarded as an amiable eccentricity, and had not been recognized at its true value. That his telescope-building activities had caused some ripples of gossip to spread out from his workshop is indicated by the fact that as early as 1777 he had been visited by Nevil Maskelyne, the Astronomer Royal, who was staying in Bath, and at about the same time by Dr. Blagden, the secretary of the Royal Society, and Dr. Hornsby from Oxford. But it was chiefly through the good offices of Dr. Watson that the musician began to achieve recognition as a scientist—first among the scientifically minded and probably rather dilettante gentlemen of Bath, and later from the Royal Society in London, to which body he communicated William's earliest astronomical papers.

The years 1779 and 1780 witnessed some relaxation of William's labours in the workshop, and an increased preoccupation with observational astronomy. William had by now acquired sufficient skill in mirror-making for his telescopes to be powerful and efficient instruments of astronomical research, and he never lost sight of the purpose to which his optical experiments and labours were dedicated: the exploration of the night skies. In January 1781, however, he began drawing up plans for a still larger telescope—of 48 inches aperture, with a focal length of 30 feet. This may have been the reason for his return to their old home at 19 New King Street two months later, for the workshop facilities at the River Street house were hopelessly inadequate.

The early months of the year were devoted to experiments with different materials for the mirror: since the tin-copper alloy usually employed for specula was too weak for a really large mirror, trials were made with steel and wrought-iron. These proved to be unsuitable, and William reluctantly decided to reduce the aperture to 36 inches, using orthodox speculum metal. But even a 36-inch disc proved, on inquiry, to be too large an order for any of the foundries in Bath or Bristol, and he was forced to undertake the casting himself.

While the furnace was being installed in the semi-basement which opened straight on to the garden at the back of the New King Street house, work was also going ahead on the mounting and the crane which would be required to lift the mirror—weighing nearly 4 cwt.—on and off the polisher. 'Many attempts were made by way of experiment against a mirror before an intended thirty-foot telescope could be completed, for which, between whiles (not interrupting the observations with seven, ten, and twenty-foot, and writing papers for both the Royal and Bath Philosophical Societies) gauges, shapes, weight, etc., of the mirror were calculated, and trials of the composition of the metal were made. In short,' Caroline concludes, 'I saw nothing else and heard nothing else talked of but about these things when my Brothers were together.' After remarking that Alexander was always willing to help at anything new, but that he quickly got bored with the more tedious operations, Caroline goes on to explain (in a passage that illuminates the reasons for her flagging musical achievements), 'And so it happened that my Brother William was obliged to make trial of my abilities in copying for him catalogues, tables, etc., and sometimes whole papers which were lent him for his perusal . . . which kept me employed when my Brother was at the telescope at night. When I found that a hand was sometimes wanted when any particular measures were to be made with the lamp micrometer, etc., or a fire to be kept up, or a dish of coffee necessary during a long night's watching, I undertook with pleasure what others might have thought a hardship.'

Experiments with different proportions of tin and copper were continued throughout the summer until, on August 11th, all was ready for the casting of the 36-inch mirror. Caroline describes how Alexander, and even Dr. Watson, lent a hand at the job (which cannot have been very pleasant) of making the mould: 'The mirror was to be cast in a mould prepared from horse dung of which an immense quantity was to be pounded in a morter and sifted through a fine seaf; it was an endless piece of work and served me for many hours' exercise and Alex frequently took his turn at it, for we were all eager to do something towards the great undertaking; even Sir Wm. [i.e. Dr. Watson, who was knighted in 1796] would sometimes take the pestel from me when he found me in the workroom where he expected to find his friend.'

The first casting was a failure: the mould sprang a leak, with the result that one side of the mirror was thinner than the other, and during the cooling the metal cracked in several places.

William salvaged as much of the metal as he could, made what he considered to be a sufficient readjustment of the proportions of tin and copper to overcome the brittleness that had caused the cracking, and prepared for a second casting.

This was even more disastrous than the first, and might easily have had serious consequences. The tale is told in their own words. 'When everything was in readiness,' writes William, 'we put our 537·9 pounds of metal into the melting oven and gradually heated it; before it was sufficiently fluid for casting we perceived that some small quantity began to drop through the bottom of the furnace into the fire. The crack soon increased and the metal came out so fast that it ran out of the ash hole which was not lower than the stone floor of the room. When it came upon the pavement the flags began to crack and some of them to blow up, so that we found it necessary to keep a proper distance and suffer the metal to take its own course.' That the events so calmly described by William were in fact fraught with danger is shown by Caroline's more energetic picture of them: '. . . both my Brothers, and the caster and his men were obliged to run out at opposite doors, for the stone flooring (which ought to have been taken up) flew about in all directions as high as the ceiling. My poor Brothers fell exhausted by heat and exertion on a heap of brickbatts.'

With this second failure William—who was not easily discouraged, or diverted by setbacks from any course he had set his mind on—decided to let things rest for the time being; and it was not until 1785 that he returned to the attempt to make a telescope of larger focal length than 20 feet.

In describing Herschel's optical work during 1781 we have somewhat run ahead of the chronological order of events, for it was on March 13th, a few days after his return to New King Street, that he made the most spectacular (if not the most astronomically significant) discovery of his career: a discovery that brought him international fame and royal patronage, completely transformed the outward circumstances of his life by terminating both his and Caroline's musical careers, and assured that the name of William Herschel will be remembered so long as civilized man survives on this planet.

Between ten and eleven o'clock on that evening Herschel was engaged on the routine examination of the sky which was part of his second review of the heavens (begun nearly two years previously) when he came across an object whose appearance was clearly unlike that of a star. He recorded the observation, 'In the quartile near ζ Tauri the lowest of two is a curious either nebulous star or perhaps a comet. A small star follows the comet at 2/3 of the field's distance.' In his paper *Account of a Comet* which was read to the Bath Philosophical Society and presented to the Royal Society by Dr. Watson on April 26th, he further described how 'while . . . examining the small stars in the neighbourhood of H Geminorum, I perceived one that appeared visibly larger than the rest: being struck with its uncommon magnitude[1] I compared it to H Geminorum and the small star in the quartile between Auriga and Gemini, and finding it so much larger than either of them, suspected it to be a comet.'

He therefore reobserved it four nights later and found that its position relative to the small star near it had changed: it was thus proved not to be a nebulous star, and Herschel, taking it for a comet, made the first of his series of micrometer measurements of its position. It is worth noticing that Herschel had immediately recognized that the object was not an ordinary star from its appearance, and before he had detected its motion against the starry background. The sharpness of his

[1] Herschel here used the word in its obsolete sense of apparent size: 'magnitude' is nowadays only used in connection with brightness.

eye is demonstrated by the fact that the planet Uranus—for this it was—had already been observed on no fewer than seventeen occasions since 1690, and by such able observers as Flamsteed and Bradley (both Astronomers Royal in their time), without its true nature being detected. This alone serves to demolish the suggestion that Herschel's discovery was quite accidental, and therefore reflected no particular credit upon him. Indeed, to describe the discovery as accidental is, if not untrue in one sense, at least misleading. In so far as it was not the result of a planned search for an unknown but suspected new planet—as was the discovery of Neptune in 1846, for example—Herschel's discovery may be described as accidental. But to call it an accident suggests that Herschel just happened to walk out into his garden one night, point his telescope at the sky, and, lo and behold—Uranus. He was in fact engaged in a systematic survey of the whole expanse of the heavens, and this being so it was no lucky chance, but the inevitable consequence, that—with his equipment and also his skill as an observer—Uranus would sooner or later fall into his grasp. As he himself explained, 'In the regular manner I examined every star in the heavens, not only of that magnitude but many far inferior, it was that night *its turn* to be discovered. . . . Had business prevented me that evening, I must have found it the next, and the goodness of my telescope was such that I perceived its visible planetary disc as soon as I looked at it.'

The discovery of the suspected comet was immediately communicated by Dr. Watson to the Greenwich and Oxford Observatories—the only professional observatories in England at that time. Hornsey, at Oxford, was at first unable to locate it, but finally did so about the middle of April after Herschel had sent him a second description of its position. Maskelyne, the Astronomer Royal, had meanwhile spotted it by its motion between April 1st and 3rd, and in his letter to Dr. Watson remarks, 'I was able last night to detect a motion in one of them, which . . . convinces me it is a comet or a new planet, but very different from any comet I ever read any description of or saw. This seems a Comet of a new species. . . .' It is significant that, unlike Herschel, neither Hornsey nor Maskelyne was at first able to identify the object by its appearance alone. Maskelyne's is the first suggestion that the new object might be a planet: it appears never to have occurred to Herschel that such might be the case. This in itself is not really surprising, since the five planets (besides the Earth) that were then known are all visible to the naked eye and have been known to Man since before the dawn of history. No man until Herschel had ever 'discovered' a planet, and there was no reason for supposing that the six planets, Mercury, Venus, Earth, Mars, Jupiter and Saturn, did not constitute the whole of the Sun's family.

The mathematicians, particularly on the Continent, were not slow to tackle the problem of calculating an orbit that would fit the observed positions of the new object. Such work is tedious and slow, and it was at first hindered by the fact that Gemini is a winter constellation and that, soon after Herschel's announcement, observations had to be interrupted until about August. However, it became increasingly clear that the object's observed motion among the stars could not be explained on the basis of a cometary orbit, which is typically a parabola or highly elongated ellipse, whereas planetary orbits are more nearly circular; and the final proof that Herschel had made an addition to the Sun's known family of planets appears to have been reached independently by Lexell at St. Petersburg, and by Laplace, the great French mathematician and astronomer.

William's account of his discovery and his first month's

observations of the 'comet's' positions and size, had been read to the Royal Society on April 26th, where it excited great interest. Early in May he paid a short visit to London to be formally received at the Royal Society, and here he made the acquaintance of its President, Sir Joseph Banks, who subsequently became one of his most loyal friends. In November he again went to London, staying with Sir William Watson (father of his Bath friend), to receive the Royal Society's Copley Medal; the following month he was unanimously elected a Fellow.

Thus did Herschel within a few months leap from obscurity to international fame. But although he had been honoured by the Royal Society and congratulated by Europe's leading astronomers, none of this was allowed to interfere with his work at Bath, which was as little diverted by fame as it had been by adversity.

The experiments with different compositions of speculum metal, culminating in the unsuccessful attempts to cast a mirror for the projected 30-foot telescope, occupied much of his time and thoughts during the summer of 1781, but this was by no means the sum of his astronomical work. He was preparing a paper *On the Parallax of the Fixed Stars* which was read to the Royal Society in December[1] as well as his first *Catalogue of Double Stars*, read the following month. This was a compilation of 269 double, triple and multiple stars, the fruits of his second review of the heavens. No sooner was this completed than, in December, he began a third review, which

[1] Earlier papers—communicated to the Royal Society by Dr. Watson and printed in the Society's *Philosophical Transactions* before William was himself a Fellow—included two on the heights of the lunar mountains and the variable stars Mira, the *Account of a Comet*, and a paper on the rotations of the planets, based on his own observations of Mars and Jupiter during the years 1777 to 1779.

occupied him for the next two years; for this he employed the same 7-foot reflector, but increased the magnification from x227 to x460, and extended its scope to include all the stars in Flamsteed's Catalogue, together with their neighbouring stars down to the twelfth magnitude or lower.

That winter was also an unusually busy one for William musically, for in addition to his usual round of lessons,[1] rehearsals, choir practices and concert direction, he had undertaken a series of performances of oratorios jointly with an Italian composer and singer named Rauzzini. These, quite apart from the time they ate up in rehearsals and general organization, proved doubly vexatious by their lack of public support and financial loss. In January 1782 William notes, 'I gave up much time to astronomy and also attended many scholars. Some of them made me give them astronomical instead of musical lessons.' And later, 'March 20: In passion week we had four oratorios, two at Bath and the same two at Bristol. April: Attending scholars by day and astronomical observations at night.'

He was also brought increasingly in touch with events in the scientific world since his election to the Royal Society, which was the foremost clearing house of scientific news and views in the country. London friends were wont to keep him posted with news of other astronomers' work in those fields which at that time particularly interested him, scientific papers were sent him to read—and no doubt Caroline often had the task of making copies of these—and his correspondence with other scientists, both in England and abroad, steadily increased in volume.

A century and a half ago there were far fewer journals de-

[1] An autobiographical memorandum of January 1779 notes that he had reduced the number of his pupils to three or four a day, so as to leave more time for his astronomical work.

voted to the publication of new discoveries, and the results of original research, than there are nowadays; and the dissemination of scientific news depended to a much greater extent upon personal correspondence. From the time of his discovery of Uranus to the end of his life Herschel was in constant contact with the leading Continental astronomers (as well, of course, as with English scientists of his acquaintance, such as Maskelyne, Blagden, Aubert and Sir Joseph Banks), and particularly with those of France and Germany. Bode at Berlin (who owned one of Herschel's 7-foot reflectors), was assiduous in his requests for original contributions for scientific periodicals in which he was interested; but William was unwilling to divert his time and energies in this way, and Bode had to be content with copies of, or extracts from, his communications to the Royal Society. Other foreign astronomers whom Herschel kept posted with news of his latest researches were Lalande, Laplace and Messier in France, Lichtenberg at Göttingen, Schröter, and Mayer at Mannheim. Schröter, in particular, wrote voluminously to Herschel; he was an ardent amateur astronomer whose private observatory at Lilienthal, near Hanover (which contained, among other instruments, one of Herschel's 7-foot reflectors), was a sort of information centre and meeting place for astronomers in Germany.

At about this time Herschel was involved in a controversy —and a deal of correspondence—concerning the claims he made for his instruments. This is worth describing in some detail for the light it throws on the condition of observational astronomy at the close of the eighteenth century and also as an indication of the great advances that Herschel, even at this early stage in his career, had made in the technique of telescope construction and use. In his account of the discovery of Uranus, read to the Royal Society in April 1781, and also in his paper on stellar parallax and his catalogue of doubles (read the following winter), Herschel stated that he had made effective use of magnifications which were far in excess of any that had been employed, or even contemplated, by other astronomers at that time. These claims were received with something approaching general scepticism, and many people thought that Herschel must have grossly over-estimated the magnifications of his eyepieces. Another source of dissent was his claim that his instrument showed perfectly circular star images 'like shilling pieces', with clearly defined edges. That such a claim should ever have been questioned may seem extraordinary to us nowadays, when no telescope worthy of the name gives stellar images of any other sort (providing the atmosphere is in a suitable state for observation); but with the instruments in general use at the end of the eighteenth century it was quite otherwise.

The readiness of some astronomers to doubt the truth of Herschel's claims was probably reinforced by two other factors. William had had no training in the techniques of the professional scientist: he was essentially an amateur, and no matter what his brilliance and his observational skill, he lacked the mental habits, as well as the special language, of the professional. His descriptions of the position of Uranus, for example, were so vague and casual as to make its detection by other observers a matter of some difficulty; this vagueness also suggested to some professional astronomers that they were here dealing with someone too slipshod and amateurish in his methods to be taken altogether seriously. If this were the case, it was an attitude that soon became impossible to maintain, as, during the years that followed, Herschel's brilliant series of papers describing his original researches poured in to the Royal Society.

The second factor was that an error in the home-made micrometer with which he measured the positions of Uranus had unfortunately led him to believe that he could detect a diurnal parallax—that is, an apparent shift in its position against the star background due to the daily variation in the terrestrial viewpoint caused by the Earth's rotation. This led him to suppose that the 'comet' was very much nearer the Earth than it was subsequently proved to be. Though the section of his *Account of a Comet* which gave these conclusions was omitted from the text as printed in the *Philosophical Transactions*, it had nevertheless been read to the society, and had tended to discredit him as a reliable observer and to suggest that he was perhaps too gullible and not strict enough in his observational precautions.

The progress of the controversy can be followed in the correspondence which has been preserved. On 18th December 1781, Dr. Watson wrote to him describing the reception of his stellar parallax paper by the Royal Society. '. . . Mr. Russel, who has not like the rest had an opportunity of knowing more of your merit, told me frankly he thought the paper a flighty one, so that your prognosis that some would think you fit for Bedlam when you talked of a power of 5400 has been verified. . . . Even Nairne doubted your power and Aubert could not help being suspicious of some mistake, and so, my good friend, you have arrived at such perfection of your Instrument, or at least have dared to apply it to such uses and have so overleaped the timid bounds which restrain modern astronomers, that they stand aghast and are more inclined to disbelieve than to admit such unusual excellence.' A week later he followed this up with, 'I have now had a better opportunity of knowing the opinions of astronomers and opticians than I had before and I will now give you the result of my enquiries. Those who are not very much conversant in these studies have in general united their suffrages in your favour. I wish I could say the same with respect to those who are well acquainted with these matters. Of these, I am sorry to say, few are inclined to give you credit for your assertions. Some, however, I have found among these, who from what you have already done and from their personal knowledge are much inclined in your favour. What! say your opposers, opticians think it no small matter if they sell a telescope which will magnify 60 or 100 times, and here comes one who pretends to have made some which will magnify above 6000 times! is this credible? So that by what I can learn, the *trade*, as well as astronomers, oppose your pretentions. Yet, my dear Sir, be not in the least dejected, your facts will be verified and the greater will be your glory.' On January 4th, after acknowledging the receipt of the *Catalogue of Double Stars*, he continued, 'Besides the doubts entertained concerning the high powers you use, I find they hesitate with respect to your seeing the fixed stars round and well defined in very fine nights. Maskelyne and Aubert say they never saw the fixt stars without aberration. I was surprised to hear Mr. Aubert mention yesterday that he had never seen your *Star* [i.e. Uranus] tolerably well defined. . . .'

In his reply to these strictures, William opened with the only comment that could truly be made in the circumstances: 'From the contents of your letter I begin to have a much better opinion of my own observations than I had before. I thought what I have seen had been within the reach of many a good telescope, and I am surprised that neither Mr. Aubert nor Dr. Maskelyne have seen the stars round and well defined. I do not say without the least aberration, for so far I will not go even with Jupiter or Saturn; but that I have a thousand and a thousand times seen them (with 460) as well defined as I ever saw Jupiter (with 227) I am very well convinced of to myself. And I believe till these gentlemen can see them so, they will not be able to find that ζ Cancri, *h* Draconis etc. are double . . . for the aberration of one of the stars will efface the other star, or make them appear as one. . . . Seeing is in some respect an art which must be learnt. To make a person see with such a power is nearly the same as if I were asked to make him play one of Handel's fugues upon the organ. Many a night have I been practising to see, and it would be strange if one did not acquire a certain dexterity by such constant practice.' He then went on to defend in detail his statements regarding the sizes of stellar images under different magnifications.

After the *Catalogue of Double Stars* had been received by the Royal Society, Watson wrote to Herschel that, as a special mark of consideration, the society had decided to waive the matter of fees in his case (on the grounds that 'the money which was withheld from the society would still be expended on such objects which would best answer the view of the society'). 'This', he went on, 'gives me infinite pleasure as this shews the great respect they have for you, as well as for other considerations. Your Catalogue was read yesterday in the manner you directed. . . . Dr. Maskelyne told me yesterday after the Society was over, that tho' he did not in the least doubt your veracity, he could not help thinking that you were mistaken as to your high powers.'

About this time William enlisted the support of his friend, Alexander Aubert. Aubert—who had made William's acquaintance some five years previously, when he called on him in Bath with an introduction from Dr. Hornsby—had been attracted to astronomy, when still a schoolboy, by the great comet of 1744. His observatory at Loampit Hill near Deptford, later moved to Islington, was almost the only well-equipped private observatory in the country at this time. William sent him a set of star maps with certain double and multiple stars marked in red ink, so that Aubert could give them his special attention in the hope that he would be able to verify William's observations of them. 'I find by my excellent friend, Dr. Watson,' he wrote, 'that my observations will stand much in need of the protection of some kind gentleman well known in the astronomical line, who will give credit to them by his own observations; give me leave to beg of you (for the love of Astronomy's sake) to lend your assistance, that such facts as I have pointed out may not be discredited merely because they are uncommon. It would be hard to be condemned because I have tried to improve telescopes and practised continually to see with them. These instruments have played me so many tricks that I have at last found them out in many of their humours and have made them confess to me what they would have concealed, if I had not with such perseverance and patience courted them. I have tortured them with powers, flattered them with attendance to find out the critical moments when they would act, tried them with specula of a short and of a long focus, a large aperture and a narrow one; it would be hard if they had not been kind to me at last.'

In the end Herschel was amply vindicated on both these counts. The excellence of the star images given by his 7-foot reflector was put beyond doubt when he paid several visits to Maskelyne later in 1782, and direct comparisons of the performance of his telescope with that of the Greenwich instruments demonstrated the great superiority of his own. The magnification controversy was brought to a head by a letter he received from Sir Joseph Banks in March, giving the news that Aubert, using a magnification of 1,000, had confirmed his observation that Polaris is a double star; he added, 'Our astronomical Friends however still hesitate at the immense powers which you tell us of in your papers and wait with anxiety for the explanation of them which you propose to give us. 1,000 is to them a power of great difficulty and how you can arrive at 6,000 of course to them unintelligible.' In his reply to this letter Herschel described in detail his methods of determining the magnifications of his eyepieces, and emphasized that 'To prevent any mistakes, I wish to mention again, that I have all along proceeded *experimentally* in the use of my powers, and that I do not mean to say I have used 6450 (or 5786) upon the planets, or even upon double stars; every power I have mentioned is to be understood as having been used just as it is related;[1] *but farther inferences ought not as yet to be drawn.*' (Latter italics my own.) It is of interest to note that when W.H. Steavenson examined and catalogued Herschel's extant instruments in 1924, he found that William had if anything under-estimated rather than over-estimated the powers of his eyepieces.

William's letter to Sir Joseph Banks was printed in the *Philosophical Transactions* later in the year, and finally convinced doubters that even thus early in his career he had carried the construction and use of the astronomical telescope to a pitch of refinement that gave him a head-and-shoulders lead over his contemporaries in the observational field.

[1] Herschel was here referring to the fact that some types of celestial object stand high magnification better than others. Thus the magnification necessary to separate the two components of a close double star is often far greater than the highest that can be profitably employed on the planets.

CHAPTER SIX

ROYAL PATRONAGE

The popular account of the events following the discovery of Uranus—that William was immediately summoned by George III, who thereupon pardoned him for his desertion from the Hanoverian army, made him the King's Astronomer, and subsequently conferred a knighthood upon him—is almost wholly mythical.

We have seen that William did not require a pardon from the king since he had never been a deserter from the army; and in fact he never received such a pardon. His status, after his removal from Bath to the neighbourhood of Windsor at the king's behest, was of much too informal and free-lance a character to justify the title of King's Astronomer; in any case the king already had a private observatory in the Deer Park at Richmond, complete with a resident observer who, if anyone, qualified for this title; and with this observatory William never had any connection. William was in fact never knighted by George III: the Hanoverian order that he received in 1816 was conferred by the Prince Regent and not by the king, who at that time was blind and mad, and quite incapable of conferring anything on anyone. It was William's son, John, who was created the first baronet, on the coronation of Queen

Victoria in 1838—which title became extinct in 1950 with the death at Observatory House, Slough, of the Rev. Sir John Herschel, great-grandson of William.

And finally, to imply that the king was set in such a pother of excitement by the news of the discovery of the new planet, that of his own initiative he demanded the immediate attendance of the discoverer at Court, is to misrepresent the actual course of events almost beyond recognition. It was not until fourteen months after the discovery of Uranus that Herschel was granted his first audience with the king. Coming events were first foreshadowed in a brief note in William's autobiographical memoranda for April 1782: 'Attending scholars by day and astronomical observations at night. I was informed by several gentlemen that the King expected to see me, and by my journal it appears that about the end of April I made out a list of astronomical objects that I might show the King.'

'Farmer George', as the king was nicknamed for his interest in agriculture and his stolid bourgeois character, indulged in considerable—if somewhat erratic and at times ill-advised—patronage of the arts and sciences. It occurred to a number of people who appreciated Herschel's true worth that, being like his sovereign a Hanoverian, he would be an apt recipient of royal favours; and it was at the repeated promptings of his more influential friends in London that he was first summoned to Court; it was, too, through their advice, encouragement, and their efforts on his behalf at Court that William finally became the recipient of George's patronage. At no other period of his life than during 1782 did William benefit more materially from the admiration, affection and respect of such friends as Sir Joseph Banks, Dr. Nevil Maskelyne, Alexander Aubert, and Sir William and Dr. William Watson.

It is clear from a letter written by Sir Joseph Banks to Dr. Watson that as early as February Herschel's friends had been pushing his interests at Court. Sir Joseph had 'frequently talked to the King of Mr. Herschel's extraordinary abilities', with an eye on the possibility of William's succession to the aged Dr. Demainbray who was in charge of the king's private observatory at Richmond. But it was a letter that Herschel received from his friend Colonel Walsh early in May that was the immediate cause of his cancelling his musical engagements and pupils' appointments at Bath, and setting off for London. Colonel Walsh had also been promoting his cause with the king: 'In conversation I had the Honour to hold with His Majesty the 30th ult. concerning You and Your memorable Discovery of a new Planet, I took the occasion to mention that You had a twofold claim, as a native of Hanover and a Resident of Great Britain, where the Discovery was made, to be permitted to name the Planet from His Majesty. His Majesty has since been pleased to ask me when You would be in Town, to which I could not certainly answer. . . . I yesterday discoursed with Sir Joseph Banks on this subject, who has the same sentiments with me on the matter.'

On 19th May 1782, 'this being Whit Sunday one of my Anthems was sung at St. Margaret's Chapel when for the last time I performed on the Organ.' The next day William packed up the 7-foot reflector, together with star atlases, catalogues, micrometers and 'everything which could facilitate reviewing objects'—as Caroline remarks in her still unsupple English—and staged to London, where he was the guest at the house of Sir William Watson senior, in Lincoln's Inn. A few days later he had his first audience with the king, who received him most graciously, and accepted from him a chart of the Solar System. As a result of this interview William transported his telescope to Greenwich, where it was set up until such time as the king and queen should be ready to inspect it.

For several weeks William found himself rather at a loose end in London. 'My love for activity', he once wrote, 'makes it absolutely necessary that I should be busy, for I grow sick by idleness; it kills me almost to do nothing,' and he bitterly resented the waste of precious time that might have been more profitably employed on his specula at Bath. He wrote to Caroline telling her that his pupils would have to be put off indefinitely, and asking her to send clothes to supplement the simple wardrobe which, anticipating a short stay in London, he had brought with him.

These weeks were not entirely wasted, however, for they saw his complete vindication as a maker of superb telescopes. 'These last two nights I have been star-gazing at Greenwich with Dr. Maskelyne and Mr. Aubert. We have compared our telescopes together, and mine was found very superior to any of the Royal Observatory. Double stars which they could not see with their instruments I had the pleasure to show them very plainly, and my mechanism is so much approved of that Dr. Maskelyne has already ordered a model to be taken from mine and a stand made by it to his reflector. He is, however, now so much out of love with his instrument that he begins to doubt whether it *deserves* a new stand.' Herschel observed at Greenwich on eight nights during the early part of June, and in the company of Maskelyne, Aubert and others, compared the performance of his instrument with the Observatory's 4-foot achromatic and a 6-foot reflector by the famous maker, Short.

William also tells Caroline of several subsequent meetings with the king at the evening concerts at the Palace, to which he had been given a standing invitation. These concerts held a personal as well as a musical interest for William, since several of his Griesbach nephews—the sons of his elder sister, Sophia—were now members of the Court orchestra.

Aubert's observations with his own telescope, designed to test and confirm Herschel's claims regarding the use of high powers, were also bearing fruit: 'Yesterday I dined with Colonel Walsh, who enquired after you. There were Mr. Aubert and Dr. Maskelyne. Dr. Maskelyne in public declared his obligations to me for having introduced to them the high powers, for Mr. Aubert has so much succeeded with them that he says he looks down upon 200, 300 or 400 with contempt, and immediately begins with 800. He has used 2500 very completely, and seen my fine double stars with them. . . . You see, Lina, I tell you all these things. You know vanity is not my foible, therefore I need not fear your censure.' He also spent several days with Aubert, at Loampit Hill, where 'we have tried his instruments upon the double stars and they would not at all perform what I had expected, so that I have no doubt that mine is better than any Mr. Aubert has; and if that is the case I can now say that I absolutely have the best telescopes that were ever made.'

Early in July the Royal Family moved to Windsor. William packed up his telescope and followed them, and the long-awaited demonstration took place. 'Last night', he reported to Caroline, 'the King, the Queen, the Prince of Wales, the Princess Royal, Princess Sophia, Princess Augusta, etc., Duke of Montague, Dr. Hebberdon, Mons Luc, etc. etc., saw my telescope and it was a very fine evening. My Instrument gave a general satisfaction; the King has very good eyes and enjoys Observations with the Telescopes exceedingly.' The following evening was cloudy, but he satisfied the astronomical ardour of the princesses by directing his telescope from indoors at a cardboard model of Saturn that he placed against the garden wall and lit with a lamp.

Dr. Watson had meantime returned to Bath, whence he sent William a stream of advice—and very good advice—in a series of letters: William must himself apply to the king for the post at Richmond, recently made vacant by the death of old Dr. Demainbray; he must see Hornsby (who had been highly sceptical of William's instrumental pretentions) and convince him of his competence and reliability, since he had the king's ear and could easily prevent William's preferment; he must not allow the king to suppose that his position at Bath was so flourishing that there would be a risk of any offer the king might make being refused; etc., etc.

The position of astronomer at the King's Observatory had in fact never been available to Herschel—though this was not at first known to Sir Joseph Banks or Dr. Watson—since the king had already promised it to Dr. Demainbray's son. But Herschel's successful demonstration of his telescope at Windsor, and the good account of him given by Sir Joseph, Maskelyne and others whose opinion the king could hardly ignore, bore other fruits: 'About the last week of this month [July] it was settled by His Majesty that I should give up my musical profession and, settling somewhere in the neighbourhood of Windsor, devote my time to astronomy, in consequence of which I took a house at Datchet with a convenient garden in which my 20-feet reflector might be placed. I went then to Bath to pack up my telescopes and furniture, to be sent to Datchet, to which place I returned immediately.'

From this passage in William's memoranda it is clear that he had not been appointed to a definite post as private astronomer to the king (with clearly defined duties and a salary for carrying them out), but had rather been rewarded for his services to astronomy by a pension from the king's own pocket, so that he might continue his researches unhindered by the necessity of earning a living as a professional musician. Seen in this light, the king's action appears more generous than has sometimes been suggested ('Never bought monarch honour so cheap!' was Dr. Watson's acid comment). Though William had built up his income as a musician to £400 a year, the grant of £200 that he was to receive annually from the royal purse meant financial independence, and so far as he was concerned that was the over-riding consideration: he was now free to devote his time wholly to astronomy, without any distractions, and there is no reason for doubting the sincerity of his expressions of gratitude to his monarch. Moreover, the value of money was greater then than now (the Astronomer Royal's salary was only £300) and the receipt of this annual income involved no duties other than to show the Royal Family celestial objects of particular interest whenever they might require it—a duty which was light enough to start with, and which seems to have fallen into complete desuetude with the passing of years and the progressive degeneration of the king's health and sanity. Finally, William was free to augment his income by the construction and private sale of telescopes. Two large grants, of £2,000 each, were soon to follow (to finance the construction of the 40-foot telescope), as well as an annual sum for the upkeep of this giant instrument, and a £50 a year pension for Caroline as William's assistant. All in all, George III can hardly be accused of having driven a hard bargain.

It is difficult now to be certain whether the idea of naming the new planet after George occurred to William spontaneously or was first suggested to him by Sir Joseph Banks or another of his friends. Sir Joseph had certainly realized the value of an elegant and well-timed compliment when in pursuit of royal favours, though in this case the patronage preceded the compliment.

Having at first toyed with the name 'Georginum Sidus', William was later persuaded by Dr. Watson that 'Georgium Sidus' had more suitable classical precedents. He accordingly wrote a formal letter to Sir Joseph, as President of the Royal Society, claiming his right to name the planet and giving the reasons for his choice. This letter was printed in the *Philosophical Transactions*, and the name Georgium Sidus was for some years current in England. Continental astronomers, however, were in general unwilling to depart from the age-old custom of giving names from Greek and Roman mythology to the planets and satellites of the Solar System, and the name Uranus, suggested by Bode, has been the planet's recognized appellation ever since. Herschel nevertheless continued to use such names as 'Georgium Sidus' and 'the Georgian Planet' till the end of his life.

CHAPTER SEVEN

DATCHET

Herschel was now launched on the final phase of his life and work. No more was he to be plagued with the distractions and aggravations attendant upon trying to live two men's lives at once. It is true that at first he was beset by financial difficulties, but these were gradually removed by the ever-growing demand for his telescopes, the production of which not only became a lucrative private business but at the same time enabled him to perfect his skill at making astronomical mirrors. With his transference from Bath to Datchet music became a recreation, and no longer a duty. He was now forty-three years old. Ahead of him lay another forty years, devoted exclusively to astronomy: four decades during which the genius and pertinacity of one man produced a widening of our conception, and a deepening of our understanding, of the Universe more radical than any since the time of Copernicus, three centuries before.

No time was wasted in winding up his affairs at Bath. One suspects that the Datchet house which he rented with so little delay was simply the first one he saw which had a garden for the telescopes and plenty of accommodation for workrooms; and that none of the domestic and non-astronomical considerations that might have influenced and delayed Caroline in the choice of a desirable residence, had she been consulted, ever entered his head. He hurried back to Bath, and within five days all his and Caroline's belongings and furniture were packed, and the telescopes and workshop equipment loaded on a cart ready to set off for Datchet before dawn on July 30th. William took the Slough coach on the 31st, and Caroline, accompanied by Alexander, followed the next day. After spending one night at the inn at Datchet, Caroline and her brothers walked over to inspect their new home, and poor Caroline was horrified to find a dilapidated ruin of a place that had been standing empty for years and could now hardly be seen for the jungle of weeds and overgrown grass that surrounded it. William and Alexander, however, were 'quite delighted with all the conveniences of the place. The stables were to serve as a place for ruff grinding mirrors. A very roomy Laundry was to be converted into what we called the Library of which one door opened on a large grass-plot where the small 20-ft. was to be erected and in looking about for a proper situation poor Alex. narrowly escaped going down a Well which was grown over with weeds, and they found it necessary to call in the assistance of the Gardener to mow down the whole that they might see what ground they had to step upon.'

For the next two months the place was overrun by builders and workmen, and eventually the house was brought to a tolerably habitable condition and the chaos in the garden reduced to some sort of order by trenching it to a depth of four feet.

Caroline was further frustrated during their first weeks of settling in by the lack of a servant, for the maid who had been engaged did not put in an appearance; when inquiries were made it was learnt that 'she was in prison', as Caroline, still struggling with the English language, put it, 'for teft'. She was also horrified at the high price of food at Datchet: eggs, she wailed, at 5 for 4d. (in Bath, 16 or 20 for 6d.); a butcher who gives short weight; the price of coal doubled. . . . 'O dear! thought I, what shall we do with 200 a year! after Rent and Taxes are deducted; the latter were in consequence of the overcharged rent (and there being upwards of 30 Windows on the premises) enormous, and notwithstanding all the labour and expense bestowed on it; it remained an incomfortable habitation.'

But however dreary the domestic prospects, and whatever the difficulties encountered in settling in, the removal of William's observatory was a well-planned and smoothly conducted operation, and observations of double stars for the second catalogue were under way on August 3rd, only two days after the unloading of the equipment, all of which had arrived safely.

Alexander's help in all this was invaluable, and by early October, when he had to return to Bath to take up his musical engagements, the Datchet household was beginning to run fairly smoothly. The separation was felt keenly by all of them, for Alexander had been constantly in and out of the New King Street house at Bath, and had always been a valued assistant in the workshop, where he proved to be particularly adept at any metalwork that had to be done, such as turning eyepiece tubes and the like. Alexander, though a lovable person, was not of the self-reliant, forceful type that stands firmly and confidently on its own legs, and it seems likely that since he had come from Hanover twelve years previously William and Caroline had developed an almost parental attitude towards him. That Alexander also felt the loneliness of Bath without the companionship of his brother and sister is perhaps reflected in the fact that within a year he had found himself a wife. Caroline says, 'Before we saw him again the next year he was married (wretchedly) and we saw him never otherwise but discontented after this our separation.' For many years he made it his habit to spend the summer months with William and Caroline, but little is known about his marriage or his life in Bath after Caroline, the chief chronicler of the family, had left the West Country.

During the first summer at Datchet William used frequently to take his 7-foot telescope to Windsor in the evenings, so that the king might indulge his interest in astronomy. But it was a difficult business transporting the instrument back to Datchet in the dark—as had to be done if William was to continue his own observations during the remainder of the night—and these visits to the Castle became fewer as autumn advanced. After George's first brainstorm and serious illness in 1788, William's astronomical demonstrations at Windsor probably ceased altogether.[1] For from that date onward the king was never in full possession of his health and sanity; mental breakdowns recurred in 1804 and 1810, and by 1811 his condition was such that Parliament was forced to pass the Regency Bill. For the last nine years of his life the poor blind monarch experienced only brief and infrequent flashes of sanity.

William's own work at Datchet, both instrumental and observational, was indeed more than enough to keep him fully occupied, and Caroline too. With his release from the musical slavery of Bath, the ferment of his mind burst forth in a multitude of directions, like waters from a ruptured dam. 'I employed myself now so intirely in astronomical observations, as not to miss a single hour of star-light weather, for

[1] In 1787 William sent a message to the king by one of the pages, suggesting that he should bring his telescope to the Castle to show George the so-called volcanoes that he had recently discovered on the Moon.

which I used either to watch myself or to keep up somebody to watch; and my leisure hours in the day time were spent in preparing and improving telescopes.' The third review of the entire sky was pressed on to completion in January 1784, yielding the 434 new double and multiple stars of the second *Catalogue of Double Stars* which was presented to the Royal Society the following December. The pressure at which he habitually worked was incredible, ten or twelve hours at a stretch often being spent at the telescope during the long winter nights, when 400 stars might be individually examined and recorded, and the positions of many of them measured with the micrometer.

The German astronomer von Zach, who paid William a visit at about this time, has left us this picture of Herschel at work: 'I spent the night of the 6th January at Herschel's, in Datchet, near Windsor, and had the good luck to hit on a fine evening. . . . I went to bed about one o'clock, and up to that time he had found that night four or five new nebulae. The thermometer in the garden stood at 13° Fahrenheit; but in spite of this, Herschel observes the whole night through, except that he stops every three or four hours and goes into the room for a few moments. For some years Herschel has observed the heavens every hour when the weather is clear, and this always in the open air, because he says that the telescope only performs well when it is at the same temperature as the air. He protects himself against the weather by putting on more clothing. He has an excellent constitution and thinks about nothing else in the world but the celestial bodies.'

Other fields of observation were not neglected. The variable star Mira was still kept under observation, as were the planets and the Moon. On 4th May 1783 Herschel noticed a bright point of light, which had 'the appearance of a red star of about the 4th magnitude', on the dark side of the Moon.

Dr. Lind and his wife, friends of the Herschels who happened to be present, both saw it without prompting from William. Herschel believed that they had witnessed a volcano in eruption, and when that region of the Moon was again sunlit he examined it carefully to see if any traces of the supposed eruption were still visible. On May 23th he recorded, 'I saw two small conical mountains, which I suppose to have been thrown up in the last eruption of the volcano. They are situated just by a third much larger which I have often seen before and remarked, tho' the two small ones were never before perceived in that place nor expressed in a drawing I had made of the spot.' We know now enough about the physical conditions prevailing on the Moon to be sure that no trace of active vulcanism lingers on there. Similar observations of bright spots on the dark side of the terminator have been made from time to time (among others, by Herschel himself in 1787), and they are probably to be explained as light-toned patches of the lunar surface appearing deceptively bright under earthshine, or as the summit of a mountain near the terminator catching the sun while its lower slopes and the terrain around are still in darkness; those of short duration may even be the impacts of large meteorites—events to which the Moon, having no appreciable atmosphere, must be very much more frequently subjected than the Earth.

The planets were also kept under observation, though the observations were often not published till many years later, when a sufficient number had accumulated to warrant it. Thus Herschel's paper on Venus, read to the Royal Society in 1793, makes use of observations from the whole period of sixteen years since 1777. During the autumn of 1783 William was observing Mars intensively, and these observations with others made at various times during the previous six years formed the basis of an important paper which, when it was presented to the Royal Society the following year, marked a considerable step forward in our knowledge of the planet. The polar caps of Mars—light-toned patches situated in the vicinity of the north and south poles of rotation—had been noticed by earlier observers, but Herschel's observations, which were designed to determine the exact position of the Martian axis, were the first really detailed series to be made. He not only confirmed that the caps are in fact situated at the poles, but made the important discovery that their size varies regularly, and in step with the Martian seasons: each cap increases in size during the winter in its hemisphere, and shrinks during the summer. 'The analogy between Mars and the earth,' Herschel concluded, 'is, perhaps, by far the greatest in the whole solar system. . . . If, then, we find that the globe we inhabit has its polar regions frozen and covered with mountains of ice and snow, that only partially melt when alternately exposed to the sun, I may well be permitted to surmise that the same causes may probably have the same effect on the globe of Mars; that the bright polar spots are owing to the vivid reflection of light from frozen regions; and that the reduction of those spots is to be ascribed to their being exposed to the sun.'

This deduction was perfectly correct, as also was his further conclusion that for the evaporation and condensation of the caps to occur, there must be an atmosphere to carry the water vapour. William cherished a firm but unfounded conviction that the Earth is not the only inhabited body in space, and he visualized even such unlikely habitats as the Sun and Moon as the homes of living creatures. This belief is referred to in the paper on Mars, when he remarks that the planet 'has a considerable but moderate atmosphere, so that its inhabitants enjoy a situation in many respects similar to ours'.

But the early days at Datchet are made notable by the completion and publication of a much more brilliant and original piece of work than the lunar and planetary discoveries—not excluding that of Uranus—which were no more than the by-products of Herschel's intense and many-sided activity. This was contained in a paper, *On the proper Motion of the Sun and Solar System*, which provided observational proof that the Sun, with its retinue of planets, is not fixed in space but is moving among the host of stars. Herschel was even able to locate, with surprising accuracy considering the small amount of observational material then available, the region upon the star sphere towards which this motion is carrying us. In this paper the extraordinary originality and range of Herschel's mind, and his ability to think beyond the mental environment of his contemporaries, were shown in their full force for the first time. It will be convenient, however, to delay until the next chapter further discussion of Herschel's discovery of the Sun's motion, and of its far-reaching significance in the history of astronomy.

In all this work William had the untiring assistance of his sister Caroline: nor was her assistance confined to supplying cups of coffee or thawing out frosted clothes before the fire. Describing the removal from Bath, William wrote in his journal, 'My brother and sister were with me, the former on a visit, and the latter to be my assistant in astronomy, in which capacity she had already acted in Bath'. They evolved a routine for observing as a team, with William at the telescope and Caroline sitting within earshot at a table with a clock before her, recording the observations as William called them out, and noting the time of each. Von Zach, in his account of the same visit to Datchet, describes how 'He has his twenty-foot Newtonian telescope in the open air and mounted in his garden very simply and conveniently. . . . In the room near it [the laundry-converted-to-library] sits Herschel's sister and she has Flamsteed's Atlas open before her. As he gives her the word, she writes down the declination and right ascension and the other circumstances of the observation.'

This division of labour not only left William free to devote all his attention to the observations themselves, but had the added advantage that the dark adaptation of his eye was not impaired by frequent exposures to the light illuminating the observing book. This was specially important later on, when so many hours of darkness were devoted to the observation of nebulae and star clusters whose extreme faintness rendered them barely visible at the best of times. That Caroline was also being turned into a valuable assistant in the workshop is shown by a passage in her memoirs: 'In the long days of the sommer months many 10 and 7 feet mirrors were finished, there was nothing but grinding and polishing to be seen. . . . In my leisure hours I ground 7 feet and plain mirrors from ruff to fining down and was indulged with polishing and the last finishing of a very beautiful mirror for Sir Wm. Watson.'

At the same time the quantity of Caroline's purely secretarial work was growing in step with her brother's expanding telescopic programme. Their well-established procedure was to record straight down the pages of an observing book the observations as they were made throughout the night. The following day Caroline would transfer these miscellaneous entries into the appropriate books, each containing the observations of a single object or class of objects—the 'Georgium sidus', the Moon, nebulae, etc. There was also an immense amount of work involved in preparing the observational records for publication, and in such tasks as reducing the double star (and later the nebular) observations to their final form of the published catalogues.

Caroline also appears on the stage at about this time as an observer. Her recollection that 'Some trouble also was often thrown away during those nights in the attempt to teach me to re-measure double stars with the same micrometers with which former measures had been taken, and the small twenty-foot was given me for this purpose', suggests that William's efforts to train her as an assistant observer were not altogether rewarding. But her work as an independent observer was later to bring her fame in her own right—not merely as the collaborator of her more renowned brother, but as an original worker in a field of her own: for as a comet-hunter she achieved considerable success, with eight cometary discoveries to her credit between 1786 and 1797.

She had started sweeping for comets with a small refractor immediately after her arrival at Datchet: 'I found I was to be trained for an assistant-astronomer, and by way of encouragement a telescope adapted for "sweeping" . . . was given me. I was "to sweep for comets", and I see by my journal that I began August 22nd, 1782, to write down and describe all remarkable appearances I saw in my "sweeps". . . . But it was not till the last two months of the same year that I felt the least encouragement to spend the star-light nights on a grass-plot covered with dew or hoar frost, without a human being near enough to be within call. I knew too little of the real heavens to be able to point out every object so as to find it again without losing too much time by consulting the Atlas. But all these troubles were removed when I knew my brother to be at no great distance making observations with his various instruments on double stars, planets, etc., and I could have his assistance immediately when I found a nebula,[1] or cluster of stars, of which I intended to give a catalogue'—a striking testimony to the familiarity with the face of the night sky that his successive reviews of the heavens had gained Herschel.

A year later Caroline exchanged her refractor for a 27-inch

[1] During 1783 Caroline discovered three previously unrecorded nebulae.

Newtonian reflector, a small instrument (little more than 4 inches in aperture) whose low magnification gave the wide field suitable for such work. After six months, however, she was forced to give up her own sweeps for comets and nebulae (at any rate for the time being) owing to the demands that were made on her time as William's assistant. 'In the beginning of December I became entirely attached to the writing desk [i.e. as William's observational amanuensis], and had seldom an opportunity after that time of using my newly acquired instrument'—quite apart from such tasks as 'to run to the clocks, write down a memorandum, fetch and carry instruments, or measure the ground with poles, etc., etc., of which something of the kind every moment would occur.'

The rising pressure of astronomical work at Datchet was balanced by no corresponding relaxation in the workshop. One result of William's fame was that he began to receive requests for his telescopes in ever-increasing numbers, and the manufacture of reflectors for private sale (7- and 10-foot[1] instruments being in special demand) soon developed into a thriving concern which very usefully supplemented the royal grant—for, as Caroline had foreseen, this was barely sufficient to live on. Five 10-foot reflectors were ordered by the king himself, and supplied at a total cost of £787 10s. (the equivalent of nearly four years' income); two 7-foot reflectors went to Greenwich; and a large number were sent to purchasers abroad. A list in William's handwriting of 76 telescopes made to private orders represents a total sum of nearly £15,000, ranging from 8 guineas up to £3,150, which was the sum paid by the King of Spain for a 25-foot telescope. Other socially illustrious purchasers of William's instruments included the Empress of Russia, the Emperor of Austria, Princess Roskow, Prince Canino, Prince Usemoff, three Dukes

[1] Apertures of about 6½ inches and 8¾ inches respectively.

and many smaller fry, as well as such scientific luminaries as Bode, Schröter, Piazzi, Pond and Nairne.

William's most important achievement as a telescope maker at this time was the 'large' 20-foot (an instrument of 18·7 inches aperture), so called to distinguish it from the 'small' 20-foot, of 12 inches aperture, which had been made at Bath. Work had begun on it immediately after they had settled at Datchet, and it was in commission by October 1783. The large 20-foot proved to be Herschel's finest instrument: the mirror was of superlative quality, and the telescope was much more manœuvrable and convenient to use than the cumbersome 40-foot mammoth that was to follow. It became William's most regularly used instrument, and with it he carried out all his nebular sweeps of the years 1783 to 1802.

So impatient was William to start observing with the new instrument that he could not wait for the mounting to be completed. Caroline viewed his impetuosity with anxiety and misgivings, 'when every moment I was alarmed by a crack or fall, knowing him to be elevated fifteen feet or more on a temporary cross-beam instead of a safe gallery. The ladders had not even their braces at the bottom; and one night, in a very high wind, he had hardly touched the ground before the whole apparatus came down. Some labouring men were called up to help in extricating the mirror, which was fortunately uninjured, but much work was cut out for carpenters next day.' However it was not William but Caroline herself who was the first casualty. On the last night of 1783 'the evening had been cloudy, but about ten o'clock a few stars became visible, and in the greatest hurry all was got ready for observing. . . . At each end of the machine or trough was an iron hook, such as butchers use for hanging their joints upon, and having to run in the dark on ground covered a foot deep with melting snow, I fell on one of these hooks, which entered my right leg above the knee. My Brother's call, "Make haste!" I could only answer by a pitiful cry, "I am hooked!" He and the workmen were instantly with me, but they could not lift me without leaving nearly two ounces of my flesh behind. . . . I had, however, the comfort to know that my Brother was no loser through this accident, for the remainder of the night was cloudy, and several nights afterwards afforded only a few short intervals favourable for sweeping, and until the 16th January there was no necessity for my exposing myself for a whole night to the severity of the season.'

Even apart from such accidents, night observation in the open air is subject to rigours with which the amateur astronomer—whose instrument is as often as not unprotected by an observatory dome—is more personally familiar than the professional. Datchet provided more than its fair share of these hardships, for the Thames valley is notoriously cold and damp during winter, and there were times when the flood waters lapped at the end of Herschel's garden.

The astronomer, even more than the cricketer and the picnicker, is at the mercy of the weather, for the mere absence of cloud is not good enough for him. If the atmosphere is very turbulent (i.e. marred by cross-currents of air at different temperatures and densities) the finest telescope in the world can be rendered unusable, without there being a cloud in the sky. William was well aware of this dependence of the 'seeing' on atmospheric and meteorological conditions, and he habitually made notes of the quality of the seeing and of such factors as might be influencing it. These notes throw an incidental light on the often uncomfortable and sometimes almost intolerable conditions under which the open-air observer has to work. 'Frost seems to be no hindrance to perfect vision. The tube of my 7-foot telescope is covered with ice; yet I see very well. . . . Not only my breath freezes upon the side of the tube, but more than once have I found my feet fastened to the ground, when I have looked long at the same star. . . . I made a number of delicate observations this night, notwithstanding, at 4 o'clock in the morning, my ink was frozen in the room; and, about 5 o'clock, a 20-feet speculum, in the tube, went off with a crack, and broke into two pieces. In looking at Fahrenheit's thermometer, I found it to stand at 11°. . . . A very thick fog settles upon all my glasses. . . . Datchet Common, which is just beyond my garden, is all under water; and the grass on which I stand with my telescope is as wet as possible. . . . My telescope is running with condensed vapour; not a breath of air stirring. . . . All the ground is covered with snow; yet I see remarkably well. . . .'

Early in 1785 conditions such as these proved too much for him. Despite the tough constitution upon which von Zach had remarked, and his own special protection ('when the waters were out round his garden, [he] used to rub himself all over, face and hands, etc., with a raw onion, to keep off the infection of the ague') he fell seriously ill. He was treated by Sir William Watson senior (who was also the king's doctor, and one of the ablest physicians of his day), and though he recovered without any harmful effects this illness was probably a contributory reason for the household's removal to the healthier atmosphere of Windsor, which took place the following June.

Herschel's first year at Datchet saw the publication not only of his most important paper to date (*On the proper Motion of the Sun*) but also that of a list of nebulae and star clusters in a French scientific annual. This, the earliest catalogue of such objects, was to have a profound influence on the direction of Herschel's thoughts, turning them towards that sphere in which his greatest achievements lie, and in which he was to find the consummation of his life work. It was increased by a supplement in the following year to make up a total of 103 objects, and was the work of the renowned discoverer of comets, Charles Messier. In his sweeps for telescopic comets Messier had come across numerous faint and ill-defined objects which, resembling flecks of cloud, were clearly not stars but were often sufficiently like faint comets to cause him frequent annoyance. It was for this reason that he compiled, and published, his catalogue of comet-resembling objects.

A copy of Messier's list was sent to Herschel by Alexander Aubert soon after its appearance, and he at once set himself to examine all these curious objects with the small 20-foot. When, in October, the large 20-foot was ready (and rather before its mounting was, as we have seen) he began with its aid to review the whole sky in a series of systematic sweeps, in the hope of being able to add to Messier's list. How successful he was is indicated by the fact that, no more than 2½ years later, he himself published his first catalogue of one thousand nebulae and clusters of stars.

At the same time, and as a result of his first examination of Messier's objects, ideas of a considerable daring and grandeur were germinating in his ever active and unmanacled mind—ideas which had as their object nothing less than the construction of the stellar universe as a whole. The large 20-foot was also put to work collecting the observational data upon which to develop these ideas. Night after night William worked with Caroline, his ever-attendant recording angel, until daylight put an end to observation. Throughout the winter of 1783 he was engaged with these two lines of observation and speculation to the exclusion of all else, and for long afterwards they remained his chief preoccupation.

But before an account of these developments can be given in a manner which will fully expose the magnitude of Herschel's contribution to science, and the new orientation that he gave to astronomy, something must first be done to sketch in the main outlines of astronomical thought at the close of the eighteenth century. For it is against this contemporary background that Herschel's work must be regarded if its true proportions and revolutionary nature are to be appreciated.

CHAPTER EIGHT

FROM THE SOLAR TO THE STELLAR SYSTEM

From the moment when Herschel unloaded his instruments off the cart that had brought them from Bath, and set them up in the wilderness of the Datchet garden, his life can no longer be considered in isolation from his work. From then on his life was his work, and almost the only 'event' that broke in upon the even tenor of his years of work at Windsor was his marriage in 1788; and even this introduced little change into the established routine of his life. One year can hardly be distinguished from the next except by the advance of his observations and the progressive development of his understanding of the physical universe. For however smooth and uneventful the surface of his daily life at Windsor might have been, beneath that surface throbbed an exciting and never resting mental activity.

Properly to understand Herschel's work and appreciate its true significance, it must be looked at in its historical perspective; and to do this necessitates a digression. At the time when Herschel walked on to the astronomical stage the interest of astronomers was almost exclusively fixed upon the Solar System. The stars were observed, indeed, but rather with a view to fixing their positions with the greatest possible accuracy than as things of any interest in themselves. Since the days of Ptolemy, whose geocentric system of the universe[1] was the crowning achievement of astronomy in classical times, the stars had been relegated to a secondary position in the known scheme of things. They were the backcloth against which the Sun, Moon and planets played out the story which it was the astronomer's main task to elucidate.

When Copernicus, in the mid-sixteenth century, replaced the Ptolemaic picture by the correct heliocentric system—with the Sun at its centre, and the planets revolving about it—the lack of any detectable parallax among the stars was simply (and correctly) taken to indicate that their distances from the Sun are immeasurably immense; and there the matter was allowed to rest. At about the time that Shakespeare was writing his last plays in retirement at Stratford, Kepler was reaching his classic solution of the problem of planetary motion; but although he cast a flood of light upon the mechanism of the Solar System, the Sun remained in his eyes the centre of the universe—not an equal member in the vast concourse of stars, all of which must be in motion relative to one another. No conception had yet been entertained of the stars and the Sun, itself a star, constituting a single, coherent and connected system.

The advent of the telescope strengthened rather than weakened astronomers' obsession with the Solar System. For whereas the Sun, Moon and planets can be effectively magnified, and seen as the naked eye can never reveal them, the stars remain mere featureless points of light no matter how powerful the telescope that is directed at them.

[1] Which placed the Earth at the centre, with the Sun, Moon and planets revolving round it, and the stars mere unchanging points of light on the outer edge of the universe.

In 1675 the Royal Observatory was founded at Greenwich. In 1687 was published Newton's *Principia Mathematica*; this contained the epoch-making statement of 35 words which defined the underlying reason for the Keplerian laws of planetary motion, and laid down the mechanism governing the motion of every material particle in the universe, from the famous but mythical apple to the remotest star. These two events set the pattern of astronomy for the century that elapsed before the appearance of Herschel on the scene.

The Royal Observatory was founded by Charles II with the specific and practical object of 'finding out the longitude of places for perfecting navigation and astronomy'. The furtherance of this task involved the accumulation of more numerous and more accurate determinations of stellar positions than were then available, and also the improvement of the law of the Moon's motion—for observations of the Moon were the only method of determining a ship's longitude until Harrison's invention of a reliable chronometer in about 1760 led to the modern method of comparing the local time with Greenwich time. Throughout this century, therefore, the Royal Observatory was devoted to the fundamental task of accurately determining stellar positions, so that they could be used as reference points by means of which to fix the positions of the Sun, Moon and planets. The stars were still characterless objects: mere points of light, each with a number attached, an assistance to the better understanding of the workings of the Solar System, and a convenience to mariners—but nothing more.

Even Newton's great generalization did nothing to change this situation. For although the law of gravitation was described as universal, and therefore applicable throughout the universe of stars as well as within the Solar System, it was only by means of the observed motions of the Sun's family of planets and satellites that it could be effectively tested. This served to concentrate the attention of astronomers on the Solar System even more exclusively than before. Newton's law did not gain immediate and general acceptance, and this was particularly true of the Continent, where Descartes' theory of 'vortices' was well entrenched.[1]

It was not until Halley's spectacular success in applying Newton's law to predict that the comet of 1682 would return in 1758 (it was picked up on Christmas Day of that year), that Newton may be said to have been universally vindicated. Thereafter a brilliant school of French mathematician-astronomers, whose culminating achievement was the *Mécanique Céleste* of Laplace, devoted all their energies to interpreting the observed motions of planets, satellites and comets in the light of the Newtonian law of gravitation. Here too, then, sidereal astronomy was pushed into the background, as being a field in which fruitful study was impossible.

The first event that foreshadowed the gradual shift of interest from the Sun's family to the stellar universe—which Herschel made plain, and which has continued down to the present day—was the discovery by Halley in 1718 that four bright stars had altered their positions in the sky since the time of Ptolemy (one of them, indeed, since the sixteenth century). The moment the stars were shown to have a life of their own, to be something more than an unchanging background against which to view the pageantry of the Solar System, then the reorientation of astronomy in their favour was inevitable.

Maskelyne, Herschel's friend (who was Astronomer Royal

[1] Herschel takes a caustic dig at the then exploded theory of vortices in his 1785 paper *On the Construction of the Heavens*: 'If we indulge a fanciful imagination and build worlds of our own, we must not wonder at our going wide from the path of truth and nature; but these will vanish like the Cartesian vortices, that soon gave way when better theories were offered.'

from 1765 until his death in 1811), confirmed Halley's results and extended them by discovering three more stars with measurable proper motions—as these movements of a star across the line of sight (i.e. motion over the apparent surface of the star sphere) are termed. By 1783 six more had been added by the French astronomer Lalande, making a total of 14 stars (Castor, one of Maskelyne's, being double) whose proper motions had been detected and measured.

These displacements are extremely small: even Arcturus, with the largest proper motion of the fourteen, takes over 800 years to change its position on the star sphere by an amount equal to the apparent diameter of the Moon.

The one thing lacking to set the era of sidereal astronomy in full stride was a knowledge of the distance of a single star, and it is significant that one of Herschel's very earliest papers was devoted to this problem, and suggested a possible means of breaking it (see p. 65). Until the stars could be thought of as objects arrayed in depth, stellar astronomy was confined to observations of the varying brightness of some stars and, since Halley, the infinitesimal movements of a few others across the face of the star sphere. But none of the tasks of the mid-eighteenth century astronomer made it necessary for him to think of the stars in a manner different from the ancients—to treat them, that is to say, as though they were not equally distant, dimensionless points of light set upon the surface of the imaginary star sphere.

That the discovery of stellar proper motions was capable of unfreezing the centuries-old gelation in which sidereal astronomy had stagnated, was speedily and brilliantly proved by Herschel. This 'unfixing' of the stars—which since the time of the ancient astronomers had traditionally been dubbed the 'fixed stars' to distinguish them from the 'wandering stars', or planets—would, wrote Herschel in 1783, 'lead us strongly to

The Forty-Foot Telescope, built 1785–9, dismantled 1839

suspect, that there is not, in strictness of speaking, one *fixed* star in the heavens; but many other reasons, which I shall presently adduce, will render this so obvious, that there can hardly remain a doubt of the general motion of all the starry systems, and consequently of the solar one among the rest.'

These 'many other reasons' display the operation of what was perhaps Herschel's most notable and valuable gift—the imaginative power, disciplined by reason, which he could bring to bear upon sparse or apparently unfruitful and useless data, so that they were made to provide new, valuable, and often revolutionary information concerning the universe we inhabit.

If you drive at night down a long straight road, lit on either side by street lamps, you will notice that the combination of perspective and your own motion produces two quite different appearances when you look out through the windscreen in the direction of the car's motion, and out of the rear window in the direction from which it has come. In the former direction the lights on either side of your line of travel appear to be opening out: clustered close together in the far distance, they separate progressively up to the time that you pass them. Then, from the rear window, the reverse process is seen: the lights close in again, being clustered close together by the time that they vanish in the distance.

It was this principle that Herschel applied to discover the fact and the direction of the Sun's motion within the system of the stars scattered around it on all sides in space. His street lamps were the stars: if the Sun is in motion, the stars in the direction of this motion should exhibit the 'opening out' effect, whilst stars in the diametrically opposite part of the sky should be 'closing in'. But there were two reasons why, in practice, the problem was extremely difficult to solve. In the first place, the stars (unlike the street lamps) cannot be supposed to be stationary; and their own random motions will be added to, and tend to cloak, the element of their total observed motion which is due to the Sun's displacement. It is easy to see that the 'opening out' and 'closing in' effect would be much more difficult for the observer in the car to detect if the street lamps were wandering about the fields on either side of the road at various speeds and in various directions. And secondly, Herschel had no more than 14 proper motions to work on.

Nevertheless, he was able in his paper *On the proper Motion of the Sun and Solar System*, read to the Royal Society in March 1783, to show how these two components of a star's observed proper motion could be disentangled, and that when this was done the optical effect due to solar motion was undoubtedly present: the Sun, he announced, is in fact moving through space towards that region of the sky occupied by the central part of the constellation Hercules.

Though the possibility of the Sun's motion had been entertained by a few astronomers before Herschel's time, he was the first man to consider the detection of such motion a practical proposition, and his proof of it was an achievement of the very first importance. The method he employed was brilliantly conceived, and considering the small number of proper motions that were available for him to make use of, his identification of lambda Herculis as the point on the star sphere towards which the Sun is travelling was astonishingly accurate. Although his result was at the time received with considerable scepticism, as being founded on insufficient data, later work has abundantly confirmed him. He himself refined his first result by the inclusion of 32 additional proper motions (supplied by his friend Aubert after the paper was read, and based upon differences of position in the catalogues of Olaf Römer, 1706, and Christian Mayer, 1756), and he returned to the problem again with two papers dated 1805 and 1806. In the latter he attempted not only to define more precisely the direction of the Sun's motion, but also to determine its velocity. Since the linear distance of no single one of his 'street lamp' stars was known at that time, it was clearly impossible for him to express this velocity in linear units, such as miles per second. The most he could do was to say that if the Sun were observed from a viewpoint situated at right angles to its line of motion and at a distance equal to that of Sirius, then its velocity would give it an angular displacement of 1·112 seconds of arc per year.[1]

All in all, the manner in which Herschel tackled this extremely complex problem of the Sun's motion, and the accuracy and simplicity of his solution, display at their most brilliant his gifts of intellectual courage, clear vision, ability to appreciate essentials, and technical ingenuity amounting to virtuosity.

We saw in the last chapter how the publication of Messier's first list of nebulae and clusters was instrumental in turning Herschel's interest in a new direction. During his first review of these objects with the small 20-foot he discovered that (owing to the superiority of his instrument over Messier's in the matter of light grasp, and also of resolving power, which, like light grasp, is dependent upon the telescope's aperture) many objects which Messier had described as nebulae without any trace of resolution into stars 'have either plainly appeared to be nothing but stars, or at least to contain stars, and to shew every other indication of consisting of them entirely'. He had already noticed, as did Galileo before him, that the larger the objective used, the more it is capable of breaking up the uniform pearly light of the Milky Way into individual stellar

[1] The degree is subdivided into 60 minutes of arc, and each minute into 60 seconds; there are thus 3,600 seconds in 1 degree.

points. He was thus drawn to the conclusion—which remained a central tenet of his cosmological thought until he was forced to modify it eight years later—that all 'nebulae' are in fact clusters of stars, and could be seen as such if viewed with a large enough telescope.

In October 1783 the large 20-foot (with an aperture half as large again as that of the 'small' 20-foot) was set to work on a programme of systematic sky sweeps whose object was the discovery of nebulae and clusters that had escaped Messier's smaller instrument; and two and a half years later he was able to present to the Royal Society his first *Catalogue of One Thousand new Nebulae and Clusters of Stars*, none of which had been described by Messier or any earlier astronomer.

It may be of interest to describe briefly the method employed by Herschel in conducting these sweeps, by whose means he systematically observed the whole face of the sky within 122° of the north celestial pole—an enormous undertaking that required nineteen years to complete.

At the start he observed without assistants, and swept the sky with horizontal movements of the telescope. A lateral motion under the mirror's point of support allowed the tube to be swung horizontally through an arc of 15°; Herschel himself stood on an observing gallery, nine feet long, at the upper end of the tube; by moving backwards and forwards along this gallery, pulling the eyepiece end of the tube with him, he could sweep out a further 15°, giving if necessary a total lateral movement of the telescope of 30° without any readjustment of the position of the whole mounting.

When carrying out a sweep he would start at one end of the gallery and, keeping his eye at the eyepiece, move slowly to the other end; he thus covered an arc of sky some 14° long and about ¼° wide (the diameter of the telescope's field). He would then make a record of any nebulae or clusters that had been encountered, raise or lower the tube by a distance equal to half or three-quarters of the field diameter, and move back along the gallery to his starting point. A set of ten, twenty or thirty such overlapping horizontal oscillations was called a 'sweep', and was entered in the 'sweep-book' with its serial number (the final sweep in the programme was No. 1112).

The disadvantages of this method quickly became apparent to him: in particular it was extremely tiring, the telescope tube being a heavy object to drag back and forth along the gallery, and the dark adaptation of his eye was continually being interfered with owing to the necessity of entering up his observations at the end of each horizontal run.

The procedure that was finally adopted involved a team of three: himself as observer, Caroline as recorder, and a workman to undertake all the movements of the telescope; also, sweeping in successive vertical strips was substituted for the original method of horizontal runs. Caroline would be seated at a table within earshot of the telescope; in front of her were a clock showing sidereal time, and a gauge whose pointer was attached to a cord running over pulleys to the upper end of the telescope, which indicated the polar distance of the centre of the telescope's field at any moment. As William called out his observations Caroline wrote them down, together with the readings of the clock and the polar distance indicator, and then called them back to William as a check; she also recorded the limits of each sweep. Thus the whole of William's attention could be concentrated on making the observations themselves. Later, when the great 40-foot telescope was completed,[1] Caroline was installed in

[1] The 40-foot, however, was never used for sweeps.

a small hut at the foot of the instrument (see Plate 3), and communication between her and William was effected by means of speaking tubes.

By the time that the programme of 20-foot sweeps was well under way, Herschel was already on the track of more important and more elusive game than previously unknown nebulae and clusters: the title of a paper that was read to the Royal Society in June 1784 (two years before the completion of the first catalogue of nebulae) was *Account of some Observations tending to investigate the Construction of the Heavens*, and shows that he was now applying himself to the much more complex task of elucidating the form and structure of the stellar universe.

In reviewing Messier's objects he had been struck by the marked clustering tendency shown by the nebulae. One area of the sky, perhaps quite small, would literally teem with them; from another region they would be wholly absent; and often the sky immediately surrounding such a clustering of nebulae would be strangely devoid of stars. Was there any particular significance in this? What was the actual arrangement in space of these 'strata' of nebulae, and what was the reason underlying their arrangement? Finally, and most fundamental of all, if these nebulae were indeed composed of stars (though too faint to be seen individually), would our own stellar system look like one of them if viewed from outside and from a great enough distance? And if it could be so viewed, what shape would it be seen to have? Was all space populated by numberless isolated stellar systems, to one of which the Sun belonged?

Such questions led Herschel to think of the stars that we see in the night sky—and which the telescope multiplies a millionfold, especially within the boundaries of the Milky Way—as a three-dimensional system in space, a coherent system or gigantic star cluster which must have some definite size and shape, both as yet unknown. How vastly different is this conception of the stellar universe from the then current way of thinking of the stars as forming the equidistant background against which the Solar System is projected. What Herschel was striving to do, and soon accomplished, was to provide the sidereal universe with a third dimension—depth. As he himself remarked in this paper, 'Hitherto the sidereal heavens have, not inadequately for the purpose designed [e.g. providing fundamental positions for the determination of longitude, or for the checking of Newton's law by observations of planetary motions], been represented by the concave surface of a sphere, in the centre of which the eye of an observer might be supposed to be placed.' But from this time onward no such unsophisticated and illusory picture of the universe was possible for general purposes—Herschel's work was done too thoroughly.

When he came to consider the problem of the shape and structure of the great system of stars that we call the Galaxy, Herschel was at once confronted by the blank wall of his ignorance of the actual distance of a single one of its members: whatever the distances of the stars may really be, they *appear* as though projected on the surface of the 'star sphere' —that is, they all appear equally distant. How, then, to discover the outlines of the great cluster which they form? For to do that would involve knowledge of at any rate the relative distances of the most remote stars in various directions.

Having at that time no information regarding the distribution of the stars in depth, all he had to go on was their apparent distribution on the star sphere. By far the most striking feature of this distribution is the Milky Way, which telescopes show to be composed (to a large extent, at least) of myriads upon myriads of stars; these are too faint and too closely crowded to be seen as individual stellar points by the naked eye, although their combined light is visible. The first circumnavigators of the world made the discovery that the Milky Way forms a complete girdle round the star sphere, which it divides nearly equally into two halves. Both its width and its brightness vary considerably in different regions, and for about one-third of its length (from Cygnus down to the southern constellation of Centaurus) it is divided into two parallel streams by a dark central rift.

How could this appearance be explained in terms of the spatial distribution of its component stars? Two possibilities were considered by Herschel: first, that the Milky Way really is a vast and distant ring of stars (like an American doughnut), which encloses a relatively starless space containing the Sun; or secondly, that the distance to the edge of the Galaxy in the direction of the Milky Way is much greater than that to the edge on either side, so that the apparent crowding of the fainter, and therefore probably more distant, stars within the Milky Way is an effect of perspective. This would make the Galaxy a circular, flattened structure—rather like a biconvex lens—throughout which the stars are evenly distributed. The central plane of this 'lens' would be the plane of the Milky Way, and the Sun would be situated somewhere inside the lens and (since the Milky Way divides the heavens nearly equally into two hemispheres) near this plane.

This, the so-called disc theory of the structure of the Galaxy, was later developed in detail by Herschel, and supported by a vast quantity of observational data, but it was already adumbrated in his first paper on the construction of the heavens (April 1784): 'It is very probable, that the great stratum, called the milky way, is that in which the sun is placed, though perhaps not in the very centre of its thickness. . . . From appearances then, as I observed before, we may infer, that the sun is most likely placed in one of the great strata of the fixed stars, and very probably not far from the place where some smaller stratum branches out from it [to account for the Cygnus-Centaurus rift, mentioned above]. Such a supposition will satisfactorily, and with great simplicity, account for all the phaenomena of the milky way, which, according to this hypothesis, is no other than the appearance of the projection of the stars contained in this stratum and its secondary branch.' At the same time he pointed out the inherent improbability of the ring theory: 'Should we imagine it to be an irregular ring of stars, in the centre nearly of which we must then suppose the sun to be placed, it will appear not a little extraordinary, that the sun, being a fixed star like those which compose this imagined ring, should just be in the centre of such a multitude of celestial bodies, without any apparent reason for this singular distinction.'

The main problem with which Herschel was concerned in this introductory paper was how to develop an observational method which would reveal the depth of this great stratum of stars in various directions—which is to say, to determine the Sun's position within it, relative to its centre, and the relative diameter and thickness of the stratum.

The method he proposed involved two assumptions: that the stars are distributed throughout space with a reasonably close approach to uniformity; and that his telescope was capable of reaching to the frontier of the Galaxy in all directions. The former is only very approximately true (as Herschel himself realized later), and we now know that the appearance of the Milky Way is a combined effect of the greater depth of stars there than elsewhere, and an actual physical crowding. Herschel's second assumption was likewise only partly true: his telescope could reach to the limits of the system in the directions of the galactic poles, though not in the plane of the Milky Way—i.e. he could reach to the surfaces of the 'lens' on either side of the Sun's position, but not to the rim of the lens. Nevertheless, his assumptions were not so far from the truth that the discrepancy prevented him from breaking the back of the problem of the structure of the stellar system.

If these two assumptions are granted, then the number of stars visible in equal areas of the sky (in a telescope field 2° in diameter, say) in different directions will be proportional to the thickness of the starry stratum in these directions: the more numerous the stars in a given field, the more distant the boundary of the Galaxy in that direction.

Herschel's technique was to select groups of ten closely adjacent fields of his telescope, these groups being distributed over the whole star sphere, and to count the total number of stars in the ten fields of each group; he then knocked off the last decimal place, arriving at the mean number of stars per field in each group. In some parts of the sky, far from the milky Way, he would find no more than five stars in a whole group of ten fields; in others, a single field might contain more than 500; in August 1792 he was sweeping an area in which sample gauges showed that about 258,000 stars must have passed through the field of his telescope in a period of 41 minutes.

He had already begun this process of 'gaging', as he always called it, when he wrote his paper in the spring of 1784, but he had not then accumulated sufficient data to justify anything more than high hopes for the future. He wisely cautioned that 'The subject is new, and we must attend to observations, and be guided by them, before we form general opinions', and concluded by anticipating the time when, 'by applying ourselves with all our powers to the improvement of telescopes . . . and turning them with assiduity to the study of the heavens, we shall . . . obtain some faint knowledge of, and perhaps be able partly to delineate *the Interior Construction of the Universe*'.

In January 1784 the third review of the heavens was completed, and though the preparation of the second *Catalogue of Double Stars* (read to the Royal Society the following December) from these observations must have involved William and Caroline in many hours at the writing desk, he was free to give all his observing time to star-gauging with the new 'large' 20-foot.

The outcome of this programme of 683 'gages', each in effect a sounding line cast into the Galaxy in one particular direction, was his paper *On the Construction of the Heavens*, presented to the Royal Society in February 1785.[1] The analysis of these soundings on the assumption of uniform stellar distribution established the disc theory on a firm observational basis: 'That the milky way is a most extensive stratum of stars of various sizes admits no longer of the least doubt; and that our sun is actually one of the heavenly bodies belonging to it is as evident.' This 'stratum of stars' was revealed as a roughly lens-shaped structure with a diameter rather more than four times its central thickness; on one side it is split in its median plane to a depth of about one-quarter of its diameter (the Cygnus rift); and near, but not at, the centre of this vast, flattened cloud of stars lies the Sun.

His gauging technique was capable of revealing relative distances and dimensions. But the absolute dimensions re-

[1] Where, as Aubert expressed it in a letter to William describing the meeting, 'it has given much satisfaction to ye learned and furnished much amazement to the unlearned'.

mained a mystery, since no stellar distance was known. The best that Herschel could do was to express the dimensions of the Galaxy in terms of the distance of an average first magnitude star as a unit; for in the absence of any evidence to the contrary, he felt that he was justified in assuming that the stars are, *generally speaking*, of about the same size and brightness. Writing to Maskelyne in 1782, Herschel defended this assumption by arguing from analogy: 'When I say "Let the stars be supposed *one with another* to be *about* the size of the Sun", I only mean this in the same extensive signification in which we affirm that *one with another* Men are of such or such a particular height. This does neither exclude the Dwarf, nor the Giant. An Oak-tree also is of a certain general size tho' it admits of very great variety. And . . . we shall soon allow that by mentioning the size of a Man or of an Oak-tree we speak not without some real limits. . . . If we see such conformity in the whole animal and vegetable kingdoms, that we can without injury to truth affix a certain general Idea to the sizes of the species, it appears to me highly probable and analogous to Nature, that the same regularity will hold good with regard to the fixt stars.' Hence the apparent brightness of a star should give at least approximate information about its distance, and all stars of the same apparent brightness be at about the same distance from us. But unfortunately the stars do in fact vary enormously among themselves in the matter of their absolute brightness (the most luminous known star is about five thousand million times as bright as the least luminous), and hence Herschel's unit of distance has no physical significance.

The idea of a system of stars of finite extent had been current for a long time, for if the whole of infinite space were populated with stars the night sky would be a uniform blaze of light. Even the idea of a disc-shaped stellar system had been toyed with before Herschel's time (by Kant, for example, and by the Englishman, Thomas Wright, in 1750), but only as a more or less philosophical speculation. It was left for Herschel's particular combination of brilliant experimental ability and facility in the design of research techniques, with imaginative power in the interpretation of their results, to provide the observational proof of what had previously been no more than an armchair pipe-dream.

As soon as he had described the structure of the Galaxy, Herschel went a step further. He had already been deeply impressed by the fact that increased telescopic power would resolve many 'nebulae' into stars, and at this time he was of the opinion that all nebulae were in fact star clusters, whether or not his 20-foot telescope was capable of resolving them. The obvious tendency of stars to congregate into isolated clusters would be, as he pointed out, the inevitable result of gravitation acting throughout a universe which was originally stocked uniformly with stars. Our own 'nebula', then—that 'very extensive, branching, compound Congeries of many millions of stars', as he characterized the Galaxy—is not unique; on the contrary, it is merely one of innumerable 'island universes'. He had discovered, he wrote to Fanny Burney in 1785, 'fifteen hundred whole sidereal systems, some of which might well outvie our Milky Way in grandeur', and the following year he graphically underlines, in the preface to his first catalogue of nebulae, the equality of status of our own stellar system and the island universes: 'To the inhabitants of the nebulae of the present catalogue, our sidereal system must appear either as a small nebulous patch; an extended streak of milky light; a large resolvable nebula; a very compressed cluster of minute stars hardly discernible; or as an immense collection of large scattered stars of various sizes. And either of these appearances will take place with them according as their own situation is more or less remote from ours.' This inspired deduction that many (not, as he believed at that time, all) of the 'nebulae' in his and Messier's catalogues are stellar systems comparable with our own, was not finally and incontrovertibly proved by observation until as recently as 1924.

The tendency towards increasing condensation, and the break up of stellar 'strata' into smaller, isolated clusters, was the germ from which grew his later thought concerning the evolution of the universe. For Herschel was a pioneer in the field of cosmogony (the development of the cosmos) as well as in cosmology (the study of its structure). In fact, Herschel may be said to have added, not one, but two dimensions to his contemporaries' view of the universe: depth and time.

The original form of the disc theory, as given in the 1785 paper, had later to be modified as a result of Herschel's gradual realization, firstly, that stellar distribution could not be taken as even approximately uniform, and secondly, that all 'nebulae' are not resolvable into stars. And it is interesting to see that the seed of this development was already present in his doubts regarding the curious objects called planetary nebulae[1] which he suspected could not be interpreted as normal star clusters. 'Their light is so uniform, as well as vivid, the diameters so small and well defined', that 'we can hardly suppose them to be nebulae'; if they were indeed star clusters, then 'they must consist of stars that are compressed and accumulated in the highest degree'. This is what Herschel apparently thought to be the case (though he prudently repeated his warning against running on ahead of the observations), but his suspicion, as early as 1785, that planetary nebulae de-

[1] So called because of their appearance in the telescope, not because there is any real connection or resemblance between them and planets.

manded special treatment, was significant of later developments.

From the historical viewpoint, the disc theory of the Galaxy and the discovery of the Sun's motion were perhaps Herschel's most important and significant contributions to human knowledge—much more so than the discovery of Uranus, though this brought him greater fame and popular recognition. The latter was a dead end—a mere fact to be added to science's great store, but not one that threw a new light upon the other contents of the storehouse, forcing us to see them afresh.

By linking the Sun with the stellar universe, and by demonstrating that this universe is at least as fruitful a field of study as the Solar System, Herschel changed the whole orientation of astronomy. With full justification has he been described as the Father of Sidereal Astronomy.

CHAPTER NINE

SLOUGH—THE GREAT FORTY-FOOT REFLECTOR—MARRIAGE

We can now resume the Herschel story at the point where we interrupted it, with William recovering from his illness in the spring of 1785. Datchet was clearly quite unsuitable as a residence for one who had at the same time a tendency to ague and an occupation that kept him out of doors night after night. Another reason for the move to Old Windsor, which was made in June of that year —and a reason that probably carried more weight with William—was that his plans for another and still larger telescope were maturing, and the Datchet garden would have been too small to accommodate it.

It had long been Herschel's ambition to build a telescope whose light grasp exceeded even that of the 'large' 20-foot. The cost of such an instrument would be far beyond the limited and already strained resources of his budget as a royal pensioner, and in 1785 he asked Sir Joseph Banks to petition the king on his behalf. This was successful (the king had probably already heard, by a roundabout route, of Herschel's financial difficulties), and in September he was granted a sum of £2,000 'Which was for the amount of the expense of the materials and of such work as carpenters, bricklayers and smiths can only do; intending not only to execute all the optical parts himself, but also to contrive, direct and complete the whole construction of a large telescope. It remained now only to fix upon the size of it, and having proposed to the King either a 30 or a 40 feet telescope, His Majesty fixed upon the largest.'

Two years later—the enormous instrument being then half-way to completion—a second grant of £2,000 was made, as well as a valuable £200 annual allowance towards its upkeep and the wages of the assistants whose job it was to impart the necessary movements to the tube during observation. At the same time an annual salary of £50 was allotted to Caroline.

The construction of the 40-foot, with its 48-inch diameter mirror, was Herschel's most ambitious undertaking as a telescope maker. Every detail of the tube and mounting were designed by himself, and nothing was so small or unimportant as to escape his vigilance as overseer of the large gang of workmen who were employed on the project.

The work had hardly started when a setback was encountered: the 'litigious woman' who owned Clay Hall, the house Herschel had taken in Windsor, insisted that the proposed construction would increase the value of her property and that accordingly the rent would have to be increased from year to year. William had no intention of submitting to this piece of shameless brigandage, and in April 1786 he and Caroline moved house for the last time. Their new home at Slough—'the spot of all the world where the greatest number of discoveries have been made'—was a small eighteenth-century red brick house, standing in an acre of pleasant garden which was flanked by elms and commanded a fine view of Windsor Castle. Observatory House still stands, though both it and its surroundings have changed since the day, 167 years ago, when

William and Caroline Herschel moved in: the elms were cut down by William to clear the sky-view from his outdoor observatory on the garden lawn, additions were made to the house during Victorian times, the view of the Castle has been blocked by buildings, and facing Observatory House stands a monolithic supercinema which has graced the landscape since the 1930s.

Caroline was installed in the stable buildings, which were converted into a private apartment for her use—henceforth known as Observatory Cottage. A staircase led to a flat roof, and here she set up the small Newtonian reflector that she used for her cometary sweeps.

The move to Slough was made on 3rd April 1786 without the loss of a single night's observation ('the last night at Clay Hall was spent in Sweeping till daylight, and the next the Telescope stud ready for observation at Slough'), and the army of workmen were soon overrunning the place: '. . . with the morning came also his work-people of which there were no less than between 30 or 40 at work for upwards of 3 months together, some employed with felling and roothing out trees, some digging and preparing the ground for the Bricklayers who were laying the foundation for the Telescope, and the Carpenter in Slough with all his men. The Smith meanwhile was converting a wash-house into a Forge, and manufacturing complete sets of Tools required for the work he was to enter upon.'

The previous October, while he was still living at Clay Hall, William had gone up to London to supervise the casting of a 48-inch mirror. Owing to a fault in the casting this turned out to be somewhat thinner ($2\frac{1}{8}$ inches) than Herschel had specified, but although he had fears for its rigidity he decided to go ahead with the polishing, and on the basis of the experience so gained to cast and work another mirror later. This second mirror, weighing 2,758 lb., was cast early in 1788, but when the mould was opened after the usual interval of three days to allow the metal to cool, it was found that the mirror was cracked in several places. Another mould was prepared, and proportions of the alloy were changed slightly. To increase its toughness Herschel added a considerable quantity of copper; this, although it achieved its purpose, also reduced the brilliance of the metallic surface and involved frequent and tedious repolishing later. On 16th February 1788 a successful casting was made of a 48-inch disc, 3½ inches thick and weighing 19 cwt.

The thin 48-inch mirror was ground and polished entirely by hand. Professor Pictet, a visitor from Geneva, has given an eyewitness account of the process: 'In the middle of his workshop there rises a sort of altar; a massive structure terminating in a convex surface on which the mirror to be polished is to rest and to be figured by rubbing. To do this the mirror is encased in a sort of twelve-sided frame, out of which protrude as many handles which are held by twelve men. These sides are numbered and the men who are stationed at them carry the same numbers on the strong linen overalls[1] which protect their clothes from the splashes of the liquid, which from time to time is introduced between the mirror and the mould to give the polish. The mirror is moved slowly on the mould, for several hours at a time and in certain directions. . . . It is then removed on a truck and carried to the tube, into which it is lowered by a machine expressly contrived for the purpose. This labour is repeated every day for a considerable time and by the observations he makes at night, Herschel judges how nearly the mirror is approaching the standard he desires.'

The polishing of the second mirror for the 40-foot telescope

[1] So that, Dreyer suggests, Herschel could more easily call out instructions to the team regarding variations of the stroke.

required a gang of twenty men. The labour was very great, and since, moreover, Herschel was unable to exercise through the workmen his personal touch and 'feel' for the progress of the mirror's figure—learnt from his own unaided work on several hundred mirrors in the past—he decided to install a polishing machine. In January 1789 a mirror of 20 feet focal length was successfully polished by machine, and as a result of this experience a polisher for the 48-inch mirrors was built; on this the thick mirror was polished very satisfactorily during July and August.

In July 1786, only three months after he had settled at Slough, William had been forced to leave Caroline in charge of the work on the 40-foot—then in its early stages—and make a trip to Germany. George III had presented one of Herschel's 10-foot telescopes to Göttingen University, and he wished William to deliver the instrument personally.

William was accompanied by Alexander, while the latter's wife and Caroline kept one another company at Slough. The brothers stayed a week or two at Hanover—William's first visit to his home town since he had become an internationally famous figure. While there he was received in audience by Prince Edward (George III's fourth son) and Prince Frederick, who was not only the Duke of York but also, ever since he had reached the ripe age of seven months, Bishop of Osnaburg.

Of his family William wrote to Caroline, 'Mama is perfectly well and looks well. Jacob looks a little older but not nearly so much as I expected. In Sophy there is hardly any change but a few white hairs on her head. John [i.e. Dietrich] is just the same as before; his little boy seems to be a charming creature.' When he had bade them farewell William had seen his mother and Sophia, as well as Hanover itself, for the last time.

Caroline, during her brother's absence, was anything but idle. She coped with the gangs of workmen, whom she detested and distrusted, calling them 'a swarm of pilfering work people'. She was also engaged in the heavy work of reducing William's sweeps and observations of nebulae.[1] And, finally, she had taken advantage of her brother's absence to continue her own interrupted sweeps for comets. William, writing from Hanover, inquired tenderly after the 40-foot, and also asked, perhaps rather playfully, if Caroline had succeeded in discovering any comets yet. Curiously enough, at the very time he was penning this letter, Caroline had already discovered her first comet. The diary she kept of her daily work reads: '*Aug.* 1. I have calculated 100 nebulae today, and this evening I saw an object which I believe will prove tomorrow night to be a comet. *Aug.* 2. Today I calculated 150 nebulae. I fear it will not be clear tonight, it has been raining throughout the whole day, but seems now to clear up a little. 1 o'clock; the object of last night *is a Comet.*'

She wrote off to Aubert and to Dr. Blagden, the secretary of the Royal Society, announcing her discovery, and on August 6th received a visit from Sir Joseph Banks, Dr. Blagden and Lord Palmerston, who wanted to see the comet for themselves. Aubert, whose letter-writing style was always rather richly seasoned, sent a letter of congratulations: 'I wish you joy most sincerely for the discovery. I am more pleased than you can well conceive that *you* have made it and I think I see your *wonderfully clever* and *wonderfully amiable* Brother, upon the news of it, shed a tear of joy. You have immortalized your name and you deserve such a reward from the Being who has ordered all these things to move as we find them, for

[1] The first *Catalogue of One Thousand new Nebulae and Clusters of Stars* had already been presented to the Royal Society, but a second Catalogue was well under way.

your assiduity in the business of astronomy and for your love for so celebrated and so deserving a brother.'

The wonderfully clever and wonderfully amiable brother arrived home a fortnight after Caroline made her discovery (he first observed the comet on August 19th), and whether or not he shed a tear of joy it is easy to believe that his congratulations were more valued by Caroline than those from the outside world, however distinguished.

The remainder of the summer of 1786 was occupied by the polishing of the thin mirror and the building of the great wooden frame in which the tube was to be slung. 'The following two years', Caroline wrote in her autobiography, 'were spent in a perfect chaos of business. The garden and workrooms were swarming with labourers and workmen; smiths and carpenters going to and fro between the forge and the 40-feet machinery; and I ought not to forget that there is not one screw bolt about the whole apparatus but what was fixed under the immediate eye of my Brother. I have seen him lie stretched many an hour in a burning sun, across the top beam, when the iron work for the various motions was fixed. At one time no less than 24 men (12 and 12 relieving one another) kept polishing, day and night, and my Brother of course never leaving them all the while, taking his food without allowing himself time to sit down to table. The moonlight nights generally were taken for such like experiments and for the frequent journeys to Town, which he was obliged to make for ordering tools and materials which were constantly wanting, (I may say by wholesale).'

In September 1786 William again tried out his 'front view' arrangement of the eyepiece with the large 20-foot. Earlier experiments—in 1776, 1783 and 1784—had impressed him with the greatly increased brightness of the images that was the result of eliminating the second reflection, but for some reason he had always returned to the Newtonian form. From 1786 onwards, however, the large 20-foot was always used in what has now come to be called the Herschelian form, and William decided that the 40-foot should also be a 'front view' instrument, rather than a Newtonian.

By the following February the tube and mounting were far enough advanced for the thin 48-inch speculum to be placed in the tube and the first test made of its performance on astronomical objects (among them the great nebula in Orion). The mirror's figure, though at this stage still far from perfect, was better than William had expected, and the work of polishing continued throughout that spring and summer, with periodical checks on its progress, for which it was mounted in the tube. During this time the Slough household had an addition in the person of Jacob, who was staying with them on a six months' visit from Hanover. Alexander also came up from Bath to see his eldest brother, but his visit was shorter than usual owing to the illness of his wife, whom he had to leave behind in Bath. She died the following January, after only five years of married life.

Progress on the 40-foot continued steadily throughout 1788. The second mirror was, as we have seen, cast in February. It was ground in July, reground in September, and judged ready for polishing by the beginning of October. The first experiments with polishing machines were made during the winter, and at the time that the Paris mob was storming the Bastille, William Herschel was busy putting the final machine touches to his great mirror. On the 24th of the following month, August, it was tested in the telescope, and 'by the trial on the Castle it appears to be of a very excellent shape . . . the polish is still very far from being complete, but I shall try the speculum on celestial objects before I polish any more.' The actual completion of the 40-foot William dated from four days later (when he discovered the sixth satellite of Saturn with it), but polishing was continued at intervals and it was not until 1796 that the parabolic figure was acceptable.

This gigantic instrument, on whose construction William had lavished four years' anxious toil and unremitting supervision, soon became a sort of national showpiece or Eighth Wonder, and a 'must' on the sightseeing programme of foreign visitors. Part of the price that has to be paid for achieveing fame is the annoyance and interruptions caused by the often well-meaning inquisitiveness of visitors and unknown correspondents. People who would not dream of calling uninvited on a painter at work in his studio, in order to inspect his easel and brushes and to ask him how he mixes his paints, have no compunction whatever in subjecting an astronomer to a similar nuisance. Even before the discovery of Uranus the first trickle of visitors had begun; after that event the trickle rapidly became a flood. 'Many times', wrote Caroline of the Bath period, 'have I listened with pain to the conversation my Brother held with his Astronomical Friends, when being quite exhausted with answering their numerous questions.'

But William's urbanity and good humour were always adequate to deal with inquisitive strangers kindly. Professor Pictet, who visited Slough from Geneva in 1786, recalled how 'Visitors often take unwarranted advantage of his courtesy and compliance, wasting his time and putting unnecessary and often ridiculous questions, but his patience is inexhaustible and he takes these inconveniences . . . in such good part that no one could guess how much they cost him.'

Visitors of a different kind, always welcome at Observatory House, were the personal friends and fellow scientists who came from all parts of Europe. Lalande, the Professor of Astronomy at the Collège de France, stayed twice and took a particular liking to Caroline, for whom he had the greatest admiration. He had a niece named after her, and when writing to William never failed to inquire after the 'savante miss' or 'l'aimable miss'. Piazzi, discoverer of the first asteroid, was another foreign astronomer who was known at Slough; and for a couple of nights in 1787 Cassini, Legendre, Carochet and Méchain, the Director of the Paris Observatory, were all there simultaneously. A trip to Slough to meet the famous discoverer of Uranus and inspect his uniquely elephantine telescope was also a recognized outing for royalty and nobility staying at Windsor, and some of the pages of Herschel's visitors' book read rather like Debrett.

William was, not unnaturally, intensely proud of his colossal offspring. Yet he never forsook the faithful 20-foot, which he continued to use for his sweeps and star gauges; and as the years passed, less and less use was made of the 40-foot. There are records of the thick 48-inch mirror being repolished during 1797 and 1798, and again on numerous occasions between 1806 and 1809.[1] Saturn was observed with the 40-foot for the first time in eight years in 1813, and the mirror was found to be so tarnished as to give a very imperfect image; two years later William tried to use the great telescope on Saturn once more, and noted briefly 'The mirror is extremely tarnished'. Thereafter it stood abandoned—a monument to the fact that the reflecting telescope could evolve no further till the technique of making silver-on-glass mirrors was invented. Seventeen years after William's death, when half a century's exposure to the weather had made the wooden mounting unsafe, Sir John Herschel had it dismantled. The great tube was laid on its side in the garden, and Sir John and his family held a

[1] The thin 48-inch mirror was, as Herschel had feared, too flexible to maintain its figure under observational conditions, and was never used once the thick mirror was completed.

touching little requiem ceremony inside it. During the 1860s a tree, blown down in a gale, destroyed all but the lower ten feet of the tube, and this broken relic, with the great speculum which still hangs in the hall of Observatory House, are to-day all that remains of the great telescope which was once the talk of Europe.

There are a number of reasons for Herschel's disinclination to use the 40-foot as much as might have been expected. In the first place, its enormous weight really demanded a more efficient mounting than the wood-spar and rope-and-tackle affair that was the best William could provide. It was a cumbersome instrument to operate, and the more mobile 20-foot was much more convenient to use for sweeping and for following celestial objects in their diurnal motion across the sky. Then the 40-foot took so long to get ready for observation (its motions required the attendance of two workmen, as against one for the 20-foot) that full advantage could not be taken of clear intervals during broken weather; the smaller instrument, on the other hand, could be made ready for use in ten minutes.

A manuscript account of Herschel's telescopes—undated, but clearly written within a few years of William's death—says this of the 40-foot instrument: 'The woodwork is fast decaying and cannot be effectually mended. . . . The difficulty of repolishing its mirror, which is tarnished, and preserving or restoring its figure when lost, is so great that if a larger telescope than 20 ft. should ever be wanting, I am of the opinion that one of 25 ft. . . . should be a step between the 20 and 40 feet Instruments.' This question of repolishing was an important factor in Herschel's neglect of the 40-foot. To cast a mirror of this weight he had been forced to add a quantity of copper to toughen the alloy, and this had the effect of making it tarnish more quickly when in contact with the air. The large 20-foot was provided, as was Herschel's usual practice, with spare mirrors; these could be used in rotation, so that observations could continue without interruption from the periodical repolishings. The 40-foot, on the other hand, had only a single mirror (the thin mirror having been discarded owing to its inadequate rigidity), and since its brightness was seriously impaired after only two years in the telescope this meant that for a considerable part of the time the 40-foot was out of commission.

It was Herschel's principle, and a sound one, never to use a larger instrument where a smaller one would do. 'A 40-feet telescope', he wrote in 1814, 'should only be used for examining objects that other instruments will not reach. To look through one larger than required is loss of time, which, in a fine night, an astronomer has not to spare.' We also have it on Herschel's own authority that the mirror of the 40-foot was much more liable to become covered with dew—or, in cold weather, with ice—than that of the 20-foot.

And finally, though it is true (as Dr. Steavenson showed by experiment in 1924) that the figure of the 40-foot mirror was indeed a triumph of Herschel's art as a maker of astronomical mirrors, yet the manner of its mounting in the tube must have resulted in distortion of its figure which would inevitably mar its performance, and it is likely that the large 20-foot gave more perfect images.

One is led to speculate on the particular work that Herschel originally had in mind for the 40-foot. On the face of it, its chief advantage over the large 20-foot lay in its six-times-greater light grasp, which gave it an outstanding superiority in the observation of very faint objects. Yet the nebulae and clusters which engaged so much of Herschel's observing time from 1783 onward were regularly observed with the 20-foot. Dr. Dreyer has plausibly suggested that since Herschel began planning the 40-foot at the very time he was examining Messier's nebulae and resolving many of them into stars, his intention may have been to use the larger instrument primarily for this work of breaking down 'nebulae' into clusters of stars; and that when—only two years after the completion of the 40-foot—he was forced to conclude that true nebulae (i.e. clouds of structureless gas, not resolvable into stars) do exist, the great telescope lost its *raison d'être*.

It will be convenient to defer until later any account of Herschel's astronomical work during these early years at Slough, and to conclude the story of this period of his life on a domestic note. William and Caroline had for some time been friendly with a Mr. and Mrs. Pitt who lived at Upton, a short walk from the house at Slough.[1] John Pitt, a retired City man, was something of an invalid, and William used to spend many hours with him in his well-stocked library. After his death in 1786, William and Caroline continued their fairly frequent strolls across the meadows to Upton, and it soon became evident that William was beginning to feel more than neighbourly towards Mary Pitt. Two years later, in 1788, they became engaged, and on May 8th were married in Upton Church, with Caroline and Alexander as witnesses, and Sir Joseph Banks as best man.

William was then fifty years old, and apart from occasional references in his Yorkshire letters to attractive young women whom he had met, and hints in Caroline's memoirs that Mrs. Colbrooke, the widow of Bath, had taken a rather flirtatious but unreturned interest in him, there is no evidence that women had played any part in his life whatever. Fanny Burney, in her diary for the year 1786, described William as 'a man without a wish that has its object in the terrestrial globe', and it is clear that he was not one of those men to whom the companionship and stimulation of women is an essential con-

[1] Mary Pitt's mother was Herschel's landlord at Observatory House.

dition of life. Why, then, at a comparatively advanced age, he should have decided to break up his long domestic partnership with Caroline, is something of a mystery.

But however that may be, there is no doubt that the events of 1788 brought a tragic change in the conditions of Caroline's life. Her entire existence was devoted—both domestically and scientifically—to William. She adored and idolized him, and had spun the whole fabric of her life about him. In his interests she had forsaken her own musical career. Now she found herself displaced from the central position in his affections that she had occupied for so long, and that she was much hurt and, at first, bitterly resentful, is hardly surprising. In later years she destroyed the section of her diary written during this time, and the implication is that it contained passages voicing a resentment which she later came to regret. For Mary Herschel was, by the accounts of all who knew her, not only an intelligent and cultivated woman, but also a singularly endearing one—gay, kind-hearted, sociable and universally liked—and it was not long before Caroline was completely won round. No doubt she always regretted her displacement in William's household, but at least she ceased to resent its cause. Her antagonism towards Mary evaporated in the face of William's obvious happiness and Mary's natural charm. Writing many years later, John Herschel's wife, after paying tribute to Mary's 'graceful and dignified gentleness . . . even in old age', went on to say, 'Miss Herschel's good sense soon got over the startling innovation of an English lady-wife taking possession of her own peculiar fortress, and she who gladdened her husband's home soon won the entire affection of the tough little German sister.'[1]

[1] Physically, Caroline was a tiny person: the dress she wore at William's wedding is still in existence, and indicates that she could have been little more than five feet tall and correspondingly slender.

For the next nine years or so Caroline lived at Observatory Cottage, and her reason for leaving a place so conveniently situated for her work of collaboration with William is not clear. It has been suggested that the rooms, originally planned as a library and study, eventually became uncomfortably crowded with books, papers, instruments and general astronomical impedimenta. Thereafter she occupied various rooms in the neighbourhood, an arrangement that she found horribly inconvenient because of the nocturnal nature of so much of her work.

Meanwhile her daytime work as William's secretary and her night-time duties as his observational assistant continued without change or interruption. The outward circumstances of William's life were, indeed, hardly affected by his marriage. There was the addition of Mary to the household, and the frequent presence of her niece, Sophia Baldwin; there was more entertaining, perhaps; more frequent musical evenings —at which William's Griesbach nephews, five of whom were employed in the Court orchestra at Windsor,[1] would perform; and he began to take regular summer holidays away from Slough, during which Alexander would come up from Bath to keep his sister company. But William's marriage left the general pattern of his life unchanged, however much it may have contributed to his inner peace and contentment.

[1] A sixth nephew settled at Windsor after the death of his mother, William's elder sister Sophia, in 1803.

CHAPTER TEN

OBSERVATIONS OF THE SOLAR SYSTEM

William Herschel's discoveries in the field of sidereal astronomy were of such outstanding importance and of such variety, that they have tended to divert attention from his long series of observations of the Sun's family, in which field also he notably advanced human knowledge. In all, he sent no less than thirty-four communications to the Royal Society dealing with the Solar System (excluding the Sun), and the vast majority of these were accounts of his own observations and his deductions from them.

It will be recollected that three years before the completion of the 40-foot William had finally abandoned the Newtonian form of his 20-foot telescope, which thereafter was used as a 'front view', or Herschelian, reflector. It was to the increased light grasp of the instrument in this form that he attributed his next important planetary discovery, made a few months later —that of the first two satellites of his own planet, Uranus.

On 11th January 1787, in the course of the regular programme of sweeps in search of nebulae, which were eventually to cover the whole face of the sky visible from Slough, Herschel chose a sweep for the newly converted 20-foot which would bring Uranus into the telescope's field; he observed the planet carefully and noted the positions of a number of faint stars in its vicinity. The following night he found that two of the latter were missing. Observations were continued for several weeks, and by February 9th he had established by their motions that two of these field 'stars' were in fact satellites.

The news of this discovery further augmented Herschel's fame. The fact that it should have been the discoverer of the planet who also discovered these moons revolving about it, appealed particularly to the public imagination, and certainly did nothing to reduce the flow of visitors to Slough. William was indifferent to the fame, and surprisingly forbearing towards the visitors—for inquisitive callers, however genuinely interested, can be a serious nuisance to the astronomer trying to get on with his work. The improved performance of the 20-foot which was responsible for the discovery of these two satellites, Titania and Oberon, confirmed Herschel in his decision to use the 'front view' system for the 40-foot.

As might be expected, Uranus was given a good deal of attention by its discoverer—even if this was somewhat spasmodic. His earliest observations of the planet in 1781 and 1782 were directed to the determination of its size, which Herschel then derived as 5·45 times that of the Earth. Following his discovery of the two satellites, he would regularly interrupt his nightly sweeps to observe Uranus as it crossed the meridian and in his paper of the following year he reported the first determinations of the satellites' revolution periods, the discovery of the extraordinarily high inclination of their orbits to that of the planet (unique in the Solar System), and further determinations of the linear size and mass of the planet itself. In these particulars he came very close to the best modern figures, deriving 34,217 miles from Uranus's diameter, as against the now accepted figure of 30,900.

Herschel's next important contribution to the then very niggardly knowledge of the system of Uranus (all of which had been contributed by himself) was a paper written in 1797 entitled *On the Discovery of four additional Satellites of the Georgium Sidus*. Although these discoveries were never confirmed, the paper was valuable as a summary of all his observations of Uranus during the previous ten years: from these the retrograde motions of the satellites were established, and the variations of their brightness brought to light. Herschel also reported a number of observations suggesting that Uranus might have two rings, each similar to that of Saturn, but he finally decided (correctly) against this. He also noted the planet's polar flattening, from which he made the correct deduction that it must be rotating on its axis, though he was prevented from making a determination of its period by the lack of detectable spots or other markings on the tiny disc that Uranus presented in the telescope.

The study of Uranus was returned to again, and for the last time, in 1815, when Herschel communicated to the Royal Society a long paper summarizing his observations of the satellites over the twenty-three years from 1787 to 1810. His considered opinion was that Uranus certainly possesses more than two satellites, and that he had observed one or more of these from time to time; but owing to their faintness identification was extremely difficult, and he was unable to hazard a guess as to their number. (In fact, three satellites have been discovered since Herschel's day: Ariel and Umbriel by Lassell in 1851, and the very faint Miranda, discovered photographically by Kuiper in 1948.)

Of all the planets, Saturn—judging by the amount of time that he devoted to it—was Herschel's favourite; and his choice will not surprise anyone who has had the opportunity of viewing Saturn with a large telescope. The discovery of the sixth satellite which launched the 40-foot telescope on 28th August 1789 has already been mentioned. The news of the discovery was given to the world in rather a sensational manner as a postscript, of telegraphic brevity, added to the *Catalogue of a second Thousand of new Nebulae and Clusters of Stars* which was presented to the Royal Society in June: 'P.S. The planet Saturn has a *sixth satellite* revolving round it in about 32 hours 48 minutes. Its orbit lies exactly in the plane of the Ring, and within that of the first satellite. An account of its discovery with the forty-feet reflector . . . will be presented to the Royal Society at their next meeting.'

Herschel was no doubt thrilled by this early feat of his great telescope, and anxious to establish its power in the eyes of the scientific world, but the postscript does in fact convey a wrong impression, which was later corrected in the promised paper giving more details about the discovery. For Herschel had long suspected the existence of this sixth satellite (later named Enceladus), and the observation with the 40-foot was really no more than a confirmation. Its true date of discovery was two years earlier, 19th August 1787, when he had clearly seen it with the 20-foot; 'but', as he explained in a letter to Sir Joseph Banks, 'being so taken up with the Georgian satellites I had laid by the observation of those of Saturn for want of sufficient time to examine them properly.'

Enceladus was observed again with the 20-foot in July 1789, when he mistook it for Tethys, and it was not until August 28th that the 40-foot showed all six satellites strung out in a line like beads on an invisible string, thus putting the matter beyond doubt. The paper that Herschel presented to the Royal Society in November contained the additional news of the discovery of a seventh satellite (Mimas) on September 17th. It must have seemed to Herschel's contemporaries that his discoveries were now falling so thick and fast that they would soon have difficulty in keeping pace with the prodigy of Slough.

Mimas similarly had first been detected with the 20-foot (on September 8th, and probably also the 14th), the 40-foot being reserved merely for confirmation. Regular observations of the satellites were continued to the end of the year (the nebular sweeps being completely suspended for about six months), and for some years to come William observed Saturn assiduously at its oppositions.

In the *Account of the Discovery of a Sixth and Seventh Satellite of the Planet Saturn* Herschel made use of observations of Saturn dating back as far as 1781 (the year of his first recorded telescopic observation, when he was living at the Walcot turnpike house). In the other direction his observations of the planet extended over the years to 1815. The paper not only describes the discoveries of Enceladus and Mimas, and gives their revolution periods, but in addition quotes a mass of observations of Saturn itself: the construction of its rings, spots and belts observed on the body of the planet, and its marked polar flattening. From the latter Herschel deduced that it must have a dense atmosphere and rotate about an axis which is perpendicular to the rings.

In January 1790 another long paper was devoted to Saturn. From observations of bright spots and knots in the rings, made during the previous year, he deduced a rotation period of 10 h. 32 m. (extraordinarily accurate considering the practical difficulties in determining the rotation visually; spectroscopic observations give 10 h. 56 m. as the mean rotation period). The paper also contained valuable tables of the motions of all seven satellites.

His Saturn paper of 1791 was given up to a consideration of the size and structure of the planet's extraordinary and unique ring system, and it is strange that despite the amount of time that Herschel spent on the observation of Saturn, he did not discover the 'Crape Ring'—that faint appendage to the inner edge of the main ring system, which can be seen with much smaller instruments than Herschel's. From observations of the fluctuations of brightness of the satellite Iapetus Herschel discovered, and reported in this paper, that like our own Moon it rotates in the same period as it revolves about the planet.

In 1793 he dealt shortly with certain belts that he had recently observed on Saturn, and in January 1794 an important communication gave the first determination of the planet's rotation period—10 h. 16 m., which differs by only 2 minutes from the best modern determination.

This important result was really the culmination of Herschel's work on Saturn, although he continued to observe it, and contributed short papers in 1805, 1806 and 1808 on the polar flattening (which he thought to be of a different form from that of Jupiter), and on an apparent unequal flattening of the two poles which he attributed to the effect of refraction in a supposed atmosphere enveloping the rings. His last observation of Saturn, in 1815, was also the last time he used the 40-foot.

Herschel's single, and extremely important, contribution to the literature of Mars came early in his career (1784) and has already been described in Chapter 7. Observations of Jupiter during the years 1778 and 1779 led him to evolve a theory of 'trade winds'—analogous to those on Earth—to account for the complex and continuous changes that are observed in the atmosphere of that planet. With this exception his studies of Jupiter were confined to a single paper in 1797, which described his observations of the satellites between 1790 and 1796. He showed, by measures of their fluctuating brightnesses, that the four great satellites (those discovered by Galileo) all rotate in the same period that they take to revolve round Jupiter; he also described an apparent variation in their visible sizes, measured the angular size of satellite II, and made the first correct estimation of the relative sizes of all four.

His observations of the planet Venus—spread over the years 1777 to 1793—provided material for only one paper. He directed a good deal of sarcasm at Schröter's recent pronouncement that there are mountains twenty-three miles high on Venus, and showed that his own very numerous observations with powerful instrumental aid were quite inconsistent with the existence of such enormous features. He correctly deduced the existence of a considerable atmosphere from a twilight effect which he observed at the cusps when Venus was in crescent phase, and also from the absence of any dark or well-defined markings. His observations did not justify him in coming to any conclusion about the rotation period of Venus, except that it is probably less than 24 days—a point on which he again crossed swords with Schröter, who had claimed to have made a precise determination of the period as 23½ hours. Both the direction of rotation and the position of the axis were, Herschel stated, matters of complete uncertainty. Finally he made a series of measures of the planet's diameter, from which he concluded that it is slightly larger than the Earth. (Actually the diameter of Venus is about 300 miles less than the Earth's.)

Mercury, the fugitive planet of the morning and evening twilight, never attracted Herschel's attention except on the occasion of the transit of 9th November 1802 when it passed across the face of the Sun. Herschel observed this comparatively rare event with care, and noted the absence of any effects that might be attributed to an atmosphere on Mercury.

From the early days in Bath, when Dr. Watson had come upon Herschel measuring the heights of lunar mountains with a 7-foot telescope standing in the street, the Moon had interested William, though his real occupation was with those remoter, fainter and more enigmatic objects that his great telescopes were better capable of revealing than any other instruments in existence at the time. He considered that although the Moon's atmosphere must at best be 'extremely rare and unfit for the purpose of animal life', our satellite was nevertheless the home of some form of life which was no doubt as well adapted to the lunar environment as we are to the terrestrial. In a paper of 1794 he concluded a detailed discussion of the resemblances between the Earth and the Moon with the words 'I believe the analogies that have been mentioned fully sufficient to establish the high probability of the moon's being inhabited like the earth'.

His measures of the heights of a hundred or more mountains on the Moon, made at Bath, were for the most part never reduced and published. His observation in 1783 of a bright spot on the dark side of the Moon, which he thought to be a volcano in eruption, has already been described. The appearance of three similar 'volcanoes' in April 1787—two nearly 'extinct' but one taken to be erupting brightly and estimated to be three miles or more in diameter—produced a short descriptive paper from Herschel. He promised a further communication on the subject, and it has been suggested by Dr. Dreyer that his failure to send it may indicate that in the meantime he had changed his mind about the 'volcanoes'. The view was then current in France that they were nothing more than particularly light-toned patches of the Moon's surface made noticeable by earthshine; and a month or two after his marriage he was visited at Slough by the eminent French astronomer Lalande, who had already written to him suggesting this explanation, and these lunar observations must certainly have been discussed. In any case, when Caroline observed another bright speck on the dark of the Moon in 1794, her observing book described it noncommittally as 'a very bright spot in the dark part of the moon; circular.'

Attention had long ago been drawn by Titius of Wittenburg to the fact that there is a definite mathematical relationship connecting the distances of the several planets from the Sun (usually known as Bode's law). According to this 'law' there appears to be a gap between Mars and Jupiter in which there should be another planet to complete the series. Could it be that this unduly wide gap was indeed occupied by a planet, but one so small that it had hitherto escaped notice? In 1800 von Zach, who had calculated the orbit of this hypothetical planet, organized a group of twenty-four astronomers under the presidency of Schröter to search for it systematically. Early the following year Piazzi, at Palermo, observed a faint 'star' whose motion showed it to be planetary; Gauss calculated its orbit and confirmed that it indeed occupied Bode's gap in the layout of the Solar System. The discovery—following so closely on the heels of Herschel's discovery of Uranus—excited enormous interest, and this was whipped up even further by the discovery of a second similar object by Olbers the following year, and then of a third and fourth in 1804 and 1807. All these bodies were proved to move in orbits situated between those of Mars and Jupiter, and it was widely supposed that they were the remnants of a single planet which had for some reason been broken into fragments.

Herschel was as intrigued by these new developments as anyone, and during the next few years carried on a considerable correspondence with Piazzi, Olbers and Bode about them. Soon after Piazzi's discovery of Ceres it moved too near the Sun to be observed, and there was a grave danger that it would be lost again. The mathematical genius of Gauss saved the day, however, for he developed a method of orbit computation that enabled him, from the few observations Piazzi had been able to make, to indicate what its approximate position would be when it became observable again in the autumn. Herschel himself searched for it assiduously in the hours before dawn on twenty-two occasions during the last four months of the year. His lack of success, and also the fact that he himself had not discovered Ceres during his successive reviews of the heavens, is explained by his assumption that the great telescopic power at his disposal would enable him to recognize it by its appearance. For Ceres is such a small body that it presents no obvious planetary disc, and can only be distinguished from a star (except under high magnification with large telescopes) by its motion.

In February 1802 a brief note from Herschel was read to the Royal Society, in which he described his observations of Ceres on the 7th and 13th of that month. By comparing it with Uranus, whose apparent size he estimated to be four times that of Ceres, he calculated that the latter could not be much more than about half as large as the Moon. In May he contributed a second and longer paper on his observations of both Ceres and Pallas (which had been discovered in the meantime by Olbers). From micrometer measures he determined the diameter of the former as 162 miles, and of the latter as 147 miles. He then went on to discuss the nature of these tiny bodies, and their status in the hierarchy of the Solar System. Basing his argument on their small size, the high inclinations of their orbits to the general plane of the Solar System, their lack of atmospheres, and the fact that their orbits are not widely separated from one another (as are those of the major planets), he maintained that they did not comply with the recognized definition of a 'planet'. Nor could they be called comets. Because of what he described as their 'asteroidical appearance' he suggested the name 'asteroid'. This suggestion was universally adopted (though Piazzi wrote to Herschel suggesting the name 'planetoids', and Lalande did not agree that it was inappropriate to call them planets). Finally, Herschel recognized the possibility that Ceres and Pallas were merely the forerunners of a whole family of such objects. This prophecy has been amply fulfilled, for over 2,000 asteroids are known to-day. Their diameters range from less than 500 miles to a mere mile or so. Vesta, the fourth in order of discovery, is the only asteroid that is ever visible to the naked eye.

In 1804 Harding (who was Schröter's assistant at Lilienthal) discovered Juno, and Herschel published his observations made during the autumn of that year. He could detect no measurable disc, and concluded that it was at least as small as its two predecessors. 'Ceres, Pallas, and Juno', he wrote, 'are certainly three individuals of the same species. That they are beyond comparison smaller than any of the seven planets cannot be questioned. . . . A distinct magnifying power, of more than 5 or 6 hundred, has been applied to [them], but has either left us in the dark, or at least has not fully removed every doubt [concerning their planetary discs]. . . . The specific difference between planets and asteroids appears now by the addition of a third individual of the latter species to be more fully established, and that circumstance, in my opinion, has added more to the ornament of our system than the discovery of another planet could have done.'

In April 1807 Herschel received notification of the discovery of Vesta by Olbers, and briefly described his observations of it; it appeared to him quite stellar, and only to be distinguished from a star by its motion.

Herschel never discovered a comet—or perhaps one might say that his only comet was a planet. He was a careful observer of these transient objects, however, and as early as 1806 he had already observed sixteen telescopic comets. Towards the end of his life, too, he made some astonishingly accurate and prophetic speculations on the nature and evolution of comets. Apart from short papers announcing Caroline's cometary discoveries, often with notes of his own early observations of them, his contributions in this field are contained in his three papers of 1808, 1811 and 1812.

The great comet of 1807, discovered on September 9th, was intensively observed by Herschel during the following five months. These observations are described in *Observations of a Comet, made with a View to investigate its Magnitude and the Nature of its Illumination*. He came to the conclusion that its changing appearances could not be explained on the supposition that it shone, like the planets, solely by reflected sunlight, but that it must also be to some extent self-luminous: '. . . we are authorized to conclude, that the body of the comet on its surface is self-luminous, from whatever cause this quality may be derived. The vivacity of the light of the comet also, had a much greater resemblance to the radiance of the stars, than to the mild reflection of the sun's beams from the moon, which is an additional support of our former inference.' Commenting upon the close resemblance to nebulae often shown by faint comets, he wondered how many of the 'nebulae' listed in his catalogues were in fact comets.

The year 1811 saw the appearance of another 'great' comet, and a long paper read to the Royal Society in December described Herschel's detailed observations of its appearance and structure during the preceding three months, and his extremely interesting suggestions concerning the forces responsible for the formation of cometary tails and for the successive changes undergone by a comet during the course of its 'life'. The modern view of these matters is, briefly, that a comet's head consists of a solid nucleus, single or multiple, from which gases and dust particles are driven as its passage along its elongated orbit brings it nearer and nearer to the Sun. This is borne out by the spectroscope, which shows that when far distant a comet characteristically shines by reflected sunlight only, but that as it approaches the Sun it becomes partly self-radiant. The extruded matter at first forms a sort of atmosphere or coma surrounding the nucleus and is then driven away from it, by the Sun's radiation pressure, to form the tail. This radiation pressure is an actual pressure which sunlight exerts upon any surface that it strikes, and which under certain circumstances may be much stronger than the Sun's gravitational attraction: thus, after it has passed perihelion (the point on its orbit nearest to the Sun) a comet moves through space tail foremost.

At each passage through perihelion a comet is therefore subjected to an agency which saps its material resources, and comets with small orbits and short periods should accordingly grow fainter and smaller at each successive return. This has in fact been observed to occur.

The following extracts from the paper already mentioned will show how near Herschel came to formulating this picture, as a result of his observations of the comet of 1811: 'In its approach to a perihelion, a comet becomes exposed to the action of the solar rays, which, we know, are capable of producing light, heat, and chemical effects. That their influence on the present comet has caused an expansion, and decomposition of the cometic matter, we have experienced in the growing condition of the tail and shining quality of its light, which seems to be of a phosphoric nature. . . . The matter contained in the head of the comet would be dilated by the action of the sun, but chiefly in that hemisphere of it which is immediately exposed to the solar influence . . .. If we suppose the attenuation and decomposition of this matter to be carried on till its particles are sufficiently minute to receive a slow motion from the impulse of the solar beams, then will they gradually recede from the hemisphere exposed to the sun, and ascend in a very moderately diverging direction towards the regions of the fixed stars. That some such operation must have been carried on, is pretty evident from our having seen the gradual rise, and increased expansion of the tail of the comet; and if we saw the shining matter, while suspended in the cometic atmosphere, in the shape of an envelope, it follows that, in its rising condition, it would assume the appearance of those two luminous branches which we have so long observed to inclose the tail of the comet.'

Herschel went on to argue that in this case a comet's head would become more 'consolidated' at each perihelion passage, and used this idea of cometary degeneration to account for the dissimilar appearances of the comets of 1807 and 1811. The extremely vague ideas then current concerning stellar distances show plainly in these words of his: 'Then may we not conclude, that the consolidation of the comet of 1807 . . . had already been carried to a much higher degree than that of the present one, by some former approach to our sun, or to other similarly constructed celestial bodies, such as we have reason to believe the fixed stars to be? And that comets pass round other suns than ours, is rendered probable from our knowledge as yet, with certainty, of the return of only one comet [Halley's] among the great number that have been observed.'

This theory of the evolutionary changes which comets undergo found further application in his paper of 1812, where the second comet of 1811 (discovered in November) is compared with the 'great' 1811 comet and that of 1807. This comet (1811 II) Herschel believed to shine solely by reflected sunlight.

Herschel's researches within the Solar System, important though they were, and bearing the characteristic stamp of all his work—a hawklike observational acuity combined with the bold exercise of imagination in interpretation—must, however, be regarded as little more than by-products of his formidable activity: delightful dallyings at the side of the broad new highway that he was driving through the unexplored regions of stellar astronomy and cosmology.

CHAPTER ELEVEN

GLASGOW AND PARIS

The years following Herschel's marriage slid by with seeming uneventfulness, but with ceaseless mental and observational activity. The *Catalogue of a Second Thousand of new Nebulae and Clusters of Stars* was published in 1789; observations of Venus and Saturn occupied a good deal of his time; private visitors and gaping sightseers flocked to Slough in ever-increasing numbers; Caroline gradually became reconciled to the new domestic order, and affection and trust grew up between her and Mary; at times of Full Moon William would often travel up to London to attend meetings of the Royal Society—Full Moon being chosen, not for any astrological significance, but because bright moonlight interfered with his sweeps for nebulae, many of which were near the limit of vision on even the darkest nights; and night after night he and Caroline forged ahead with their work of sweeping and gauging, slowly and systematically covering every square degree of the sky visible from the garden lawn at Slough. But in attempting to reconstruct the domestic background of these years the biographer finds himself keenly regretting that nine-year period of Caroline's diary which she later saw fit to destroy.

The last decade of the eighteenth century was the busiest and most fruitful period of Caroline's life so far as her own independent work was concerned. In the observational field it yielded a crop of comets that would have been a credit to anyone: a total of eight discoveries in little more than ten years. Caroline's first comet, it will be remembered, was discovered soon after their arrival at Slough, while William was visiting Göttingen and Hanover. Seven months after his marriage, while she was engaged in hunting for the comet of 1661, whose return was expected at that time, she made her second discovery. She wrote to Maskelyne at Greenwich, giving its position and adding, 'I beg favour of you to take it under your protection'. Two more telescopic comets fell into her bag during 1790: one in January, which was faint and soon faded from sight; and one in April, regarding which she wrote to their friend Aubert, 'I found last night, at 16 h. 24 m. sidereal time, a comet and do not know what to do with it'.

The following winter a larger comet sweeper which William had been making for her was completed: this was a 5-foot Newtonian of 9·2 inches aperture. A year later, on 15th December 1791, it scored its first success. Her sixth comet, in 1793, had already been observed by Messier ten days before she first saw it, though of this she was unaware at the time. The next discovery, in November 1795, was of particular interest, for it was the second recorded appearance of the object now known as Encke's comet. This had first been observed by Méchain in 1786, but it was not until 1819 that Encke proved that both Méchain's and Caroline's observations had been of the same comet, which revolves round the Sun in the unusually short period of 3¾ years.

Caroline's eighth and last cometary discovery was made on 14th August 1797: the comet was already very bright at the time of its discovery, being clearly visible to the naked eye, and it was in fact discovered independently by two other observers on the same evening. Though she discovered no more comets after this, Caroline continued to observe these objects for many years, and the last entry in her observing book—made on 31st January 1824, after she had retired to Hanover—refers to a comet that was visible at that time.

Towards the end of the century Caroline was also busy with the enormous task of indexing Flamsteed's Star Catalogue. This great work, which had been published in 1725, six years after Flamsteed's death, was the Royal Observatory's first major contribution to astronomy. It contained the accurate positions of nearly 3,000 stars, and for many years after its appearance it was regarded as a sort of astronomer's bible, whose accuracy in even the smallest detail might not be questioned. During his reviews of the heavens, however, Herschel had encountered numerous discrepancies between the catalogue and the observed face of the sky: some of Flamsteed's stars appeared to have vanished, other stars to have come into existence since the catalogue was compiled, and many others to have changed their brightness. In attempting to trace the origin of such discrepancies Herschel had constantly to refer back to the original observations on which the catalogue entries were based. These however were published in a separate volume, and what he urgently needed was an index of cross references. In the preface to his third photometric catalogue, written in April 1797, he tells how 'I recommended it to my Sister to undertake the arduous task. At my request, and according to a plan which I laid down, she began the work about twenty months ago, and has lately finished it.' Caroline's *Index to Flamsteed's Observations of the Fixed Stars* was read to the Royal Society in March 1798; she also compiled a catalogue of 560 stars not included in Flamsteed's, which had been presented to the Royal Society the previous year.

On 7th March 1792 was born William and Mary Herschel's only child, John Frederick William, and their old friend Dr. William Watson was chosen as one of his godfathers. In the same year William was honoured by both the French Academy (which voted him their award of 1,200 livres, or about £720) and by Glasgow University, which conferred upon him the degree of LL.D. (Edinburgh University had paid him the same mark of respect six years previously.) William decided to have a break from his labours, and travel up to Scotland to receive the degree in person. His companion on this trip was a Polish friend, General Komarzewski, a man of scientific tastes who was also young John Herschel's godfather.

From the early 1790s onward William fell into the habit of taking summer holidays away from Slough—accompanied by his wife, and often by Sophia Baldwin—but of only two of these do we possess any record other than bare notes of places visited, distances covered, and the bills of the various inns where they stopped on their way. These two exceptions were the Glasgow trip of 1792, and the visit to Paris ten years later.

Herschel and General Komarzewski set off from Slough by carriage at the end of May, and followed a leisurely sightseeing route which did not bring them to Glasgow until June 29th. On the way they spent considerable time in the Midlands, visiting industrial plant of all types. The General was interested in chemistry, and also owned mines in Galicia, while William's personal interest in these visits is shown by the careful notes and numerous sketches of machinery that he made in his journal of the tour.

At Birmingham they dined with James Watt[1] (of steam-

[1] Watt did not invent the steam engine: the earliest engine known to have been actually constructed was that of Savery, in 1710. Watt's greatest contribution to steam-engine design was a device for the separate condensation of the steam (patented in 1769), which effected a great gain in mechanical efficiency.

engine fame) and were shown over the great Soho Engineering Works, with whose founder, Boulton, Watt was then in partnership. On their return journey they again visited Soho, and in after years James Watt and his wife visited the Herschels at Slough on a number of occasions. The harnessing of the power of steam was, in 1792, still a recent enough development for William to make a special note in his journal of every steam engine that they encountered on their way; the following is a typical example: 'In our first stage I saw a common steam engine. Upon the piston was kept a coat of water to prevent its losing steam. The condensation was made in the cylinder itself, by a pipe entering the bottom to inject cold water. The pressure of the atmosphere brought down the piston and the steam lifted it up.' These technical descriptions of machinery alternate strangely with rhapsodic descriptions of the Welsh countryside (they tried to climb Snowdon, but after two miles were halted by thick mist) and notes of visits to historic spots. At Edinburgh, for example, he saw 'the Castle where Queen Mary resided; the furniture which was there in her time; the bedroom and little dressing room where David Rizzio was found with the Queen; the place where he was killed. They show the stains on the floor said to be made by his blood'; and at Stratford, 'We saw the House where Shakespear lived and his chair'.

In return for the revelations of cotton spinning, iron and lead smelting, and glass making which were vouchsafed to the travellers, Herschel would on occasion produce the 7-foot reflector which was part of his baggage and introduce his hosts to Jupiter and other celestial show-pieces.

Their four days at Glasgow were fully occupied with civic and University junketings. Both William and the General were presented with the freedom of the city by the Lord Provost; and later they were entertained to an official dinner by the Principal and Professors of the University, after which the diploma of Doctor of Laws was formally presented to Herschel.

From Glasgow they struck eastward to Edinburgh, where they were again taken up with sightseeing and introductions to the local celebrities in the world of science and art. Herschel also visited the Observatory and examined its equipment. The return journey took them through the eastern counties to Sunderland; here, however, 'I could find no trace of my former habitation in that place': this must have been a nostalgic pilgrimage for William—it was then thirty-two years since, as trainer of the Durham militia band, he had moved into lodgings there. Calls were made on old friends at Richmond, Thornhill and elsewhere on the journey south, and they finally reached Slough on July 19th. William's taste for travel seems to have been whetted rather than satisfied by the trip, however, for three days later he and the General were off again on a fortnight's tour of Devon and Cornwall.

This same year, 1792, William heard of the death in Hanover of Jacob, his eldest brother and the companion of his first years in England. Early the next year a second death occurred in the family—that of the young Paul Adee Pitt, William's stepson. In April 1793 Herschel confirmed his break with his homeland by becoming naturalized; his motive was probably the desire that his son should not be a foreigner in the land of his birth.

Life continued uneventfully, the years slipping gently into the past, little noticed beneath the unvarying routine of work, the periodical repolishings of the 48-inch mirror, a new cometary discovery by Caroline, the entertainment of friends and occasional trips to London, and the longer holidays each summer. In 1793 William was elected a member of the Imperial Leopold Academy of Science, and the diploma was forwarded to him by Schröter. In 1799 Caroline made one of her rare journeys from home, going to stay with Dr. and Mrs. Maskelyne at Greenwich Observatory, where she was almost fatiguingly entertained by these old friends. The next year she again laid aside her astronomical labours for a while, and went down to Bath to straighten out the contents of a house that Mary Herschel had rented there, and which it was her intention to occupy the following winter. This task completed, she stayed on for several months in Bath, returning to Slough in November.

William had, during that summer, been intensively engaged on a brilliant series of researches into the nature of the Sun's radiation; but after Caroline's return from Bath, brother and sister once again settled down to their familiar routine of nightly sweeps and star gauges with the 20-foot reflector. The year 1802 saw the completion of this work: nineteen years of observing on a single programme, during which 1,112 individual sweeps had covered the whole visible expanse of sky, and had yielded a crop of nearly 3,000 nebulae and clusters where only about 150 had been known when the work began.

A new interest was added to Caroline's life in 1802 by her encounter at Windsor with a certain Mme. Beckedorff, a member of the Queen's household. More than a quarter of a century earlier, this lady had been a fellow pupil of Caroline's at Mme. Kustner's sewing and dressmaking classes in Hanover—those classes which Caroline had been permitted to attend on the strict understanding that whatever skill she might acquire should be applied exclusively to her brother Jacob's wardrobe. From 1802 until Mme. Beckedorff returned to Hanover seventeen years later she was one of Caroline's closest and most cherished friends. Through her, too, Caroline was brought into closer contact with the royal household; and this indomitable, unassuming, sharp-witted, and still so obviously German woman, with her strangely masculine vocation, became an established favourite with the Princesses at Windsor.

Since Louis XVI had gone to the guillotine in 1793, the war between France and England had made any intercourse between the two countries difficult, though Herschel had been able to maintain desultory contact with his French correspondents. It was from the most regular of these, Lalande, that he learnt in 1801 that he was among the first twenty-four foreign associates to be elected to the French National Institute. When the short-lived Peace of Amiens made travel between the two countries possible once again, Herschel, in common with many of his compatriots, decided to visit Paris. And on 13th July 1802 he set off in company with Mary Herschel, their ten-year-old son John, and Mary's niece, Sophia Baldwin. It is curious that Caroline never accompanied the family on their summer holidays; on this occasion, too, she remained at Slough.

Paris was crowded to overflowing with visitors, and, relieved from the stress of war, was even gayer than it is habitually supposed to be. This time, too, Herschel was visiting the city not as an unknown music teacher but as one of the most famous scientists of his day. Their fortnight's stay was a continuous round of entertainment, visiting and sightseeing. They went to the opera, the ballet and the theatre; they dined in the Jardin des Tuileries, with General Komarzewski, who also was in Paris at the time; they visited the Jardin des Plantes, and the site where the Bastille had stood until its destruction in 1789; Herschel attended meetings of the Institute, and met Méchain, Legendre, Messier and other astronomers with whom he had been corresponding for years. He and his wife dined and breakfasted several times with Laplace, the great mathematician-astronomer and author of the

Mécanique Céleste ('His lady received company abed, which to those who are not used to it appears very remarkable'). In company with Sir Charles Blagden (who as plain Dr. Blagden, Secretary of the Royal Society, had first made William's acquaintance at Bath many years before) he inspected the Paris Observatory.

The social highspot of the holiday was his audience with Napoleon, who since his return from Egypt in 1799 had been styled the First Consul. After dinner, as the guest of the Minister of the Interior, Herschel, with Laplace and Count Rumford, was conducted by him to the Palace of Malmaison which was Napoleon's residence. Herschel's journal contains a detailed account of the meeting, carefully noting the subjects of conversation (which ranged from astronomy to horse breeding and the inferiority of the English to the French police), and even the temperature and the quality of the ice-creams. But it is impossible to discover from his curiously noncommittal account what was his private opinion of the man who was so soon to set all Europe by the ears.

The last entry in the Paris journal refers to a second meeting with Messier, the famous discoverer of comets whose catalogue of 103 nebulae and clusters, published in 1783-4, had had so decisive an influence on Herschel's career, and with whom he had corresponded for many years. Poor Messier 'complained of having suffered much from his accident of falling into an ice-cellar. He is still very assiduous in observing, and regretted that he had not interest enough to get the windows mended in a kind of tower[1] where his instruments are, but keeps his spirits.'

The party returned to Slough via Dover on August 14th, and William was never again to set foot outside England.

[1] Part of the now ruined Abbey of Cluny, in Paris.

CHAPTER TWELVE

SOLAR AND STELLAR INVESTIGATIONS AFTER 1794

It will be convenient to group Herschel's later contributions to solar and sidereal astronomy under their various headings, and to describe each in turn: the nature of the Sun, and Herschel's experimental investigations of its radiation; studies of the brightness of the stars; observations of double stars, and the discovery of binary systems.

It is nowadays rather easy to forget how little was known of the actual compositions, physical conditions and natures of the heavenly bodies before the advent of the spectroscope —an instrument which for the last hundred years has ranked with the telescope (and, more recently, the camera) as the astronomer's most powerful assistant in deciphering the hieroglyphs of the universe. The Sun had been brought within the scope of scientific investigation by the invention of the telescope, and the first discovery of note—that of the sunspots—had been made in the early years of the seventeenth century. Later observers added to the sum of purely descriptive knowledge of the Sun's surface, but the nature of the spots remained for many years the subject of heated controversy. Were they solid bodies revolving close to the Sun's surface, dark clouds, smoke from solar volcanoes, patches of scum or solid objects floating, and from time to time submerging, in the Sun's liquid surface? These and many other curious suggestions were made, and it was not until 1774 that Alexander Wilson, Professor of Astronomy at Glasgow University,[1] put an end to the matter by proving that sunspots are depressions or holes in the glowing outer levels of the Sun, through which the cooler, and therefore darker, interior can be seen. Herschel was brought to this same conclusion by his observations of the great sunspot of 1783, and in his paper *On the Nature and Construction of the Sun and fixed Stars*, published in the *Philosophical Transactions* in 1795, he developed very forcibly the theory that he based on this and other observations.

The spots were clearly depressions in an outer luminous envelope, and through their central holes the dark lower levels are revealed. Herschel explained all the appearances then known by supposing that the Sun's atmosphere consists of two distinct layers: the upper, or photosphere, is made up of luminous clouds, generated by the solar atmosphere in some manner analogous to the formation of clouds in our own terrestrial atmosphere; the lower consists of dense, non-incandescent 'planetary' clouds which reflect back to us the light and heat falling upon them from the photosphere, and at the same time protect the solid surface of the Sun from this blaze of light and blast of heat.[2] The rents in this blanket of cloud, which appear to us as sunspots, are caused by atmo-

[1] The father of Patrick Wilson, an intimate friend of the Herschels, who with his sister paid numerous visits to Slough.

[2] In fact, the sunspots are not dark at all, and only appear so by contrast with their very much more brilliant surroundings. But this was not discovered till many years later, when Dawes observed a spot through a tiny diaphragm which hid all the photosphere around it, and found that the spot was not dark, but brilliantly bright.

spheric currents akin to terrestrial cyclones. Herschel surmised that the Moon and all the planets emit some light of their own, in addition to what they reflect from the Sun; thus he explained the visibility of the 'dark' side of the crescent Venus, and the brightness of the totally eclipsed Moon. The Sun he saw as, essentially, an overgrown planet with an abnormally luminous atmosphere. 'The sun, viewed in this light, appears to be nothing else than a very eminent, large, and lucid planet, evidently the first, or in strictness of speaking, the only primary one of our system; all others being truly secondary to it. Its similarity to the other globes of the solar system with regard to its solidity, its atmosphere, and its diversified surface; the rotation upon its axis, and the fall of heavy bodies, leads us on to suppose that it is most probably inhabited, like the rest of the planets, by beings whose organs are adapted to the peculiar circumstances of that vast globe.'

These general conclusions were reinforced in his long and very circumstantial second paper on the subject, read to the Royal Society in 1801. He quoted observations of his own which demonstrate that almost no feature of the Sun's surface escaped him, and he gave a detailed account of the growth and decay of a typical spot which could hardly be improved upon to-day. The meteorology of the Sun's atmosphere, in the light of these observations, was discussed with his usual vigour, and the observational material made to yield the maximum that could be legitimately deduced from it. An example of Herschel's intellectual boldness is his attempt to correlate the vagaries of the Earth's climate with the fluctuating spottedness of the Sun. Since the necessary meteorological records did not then exist, Herschel was forced back on a characteristically ingenious subterfuge: to utilize the prices of wheat at Windsor (records of which were available) as an index of the annual harvests and therefore of the average weather in different years. In his inquiry into the records of solar spottedness from 1650 onward, Herschel must have come within an ace of discovering the 11-year periodicity of sun-spot activity—a discovery that had to await the diligent observations of Schwabe in 1843.

This bold attempt to trace the effect of solar changes upon the conditions of our own planet was not without its penalties for Herschel. Brougham (who later attacked him viciously over his naming of the asteroids) described it in the *Edinburgh Review* as a 'hasty and erroneous theory', and one than which 'since the publication of Gulliver's voyage to Laputa, nothing so ridiculous has ever been offered to the world'. It also added to his undeserved and undesired reputation among the ignorant as a weather prophet, to which he referred in the pleasantly elaborate peroration of a letter written to the Earl of Salisbury in 1789: 'The papers have ascribed to me a foreknowledge of the weather, My Lord, which I am not so happy as to be in possession of: and I should be glad if I could foretell a speedy end to the present frost; which I can assure your Lordship, does not much agree with my feelings; as the number of additional Cloaths and Pellices, when I am observing, is pretty burdensome to the shoulders of

My Lord, your most obedt
and most humble servant
Wm. Herschel.'

Herschel showed great ingenuity and diligence in countering anticipated criticisms of his solar theory (the criticism, for example, that in view of the heat we receive from the Sun at our distance from it of many millions of miles, the inhabitants of the Sun's own surface would not be protected by a mere blanket of cloud from being roasted) and a brief summary of his conclusions, such as this is, can do no justice to the originality, fertility and cogency of reasoning that are displayed in these two papers.

If Herschel's views on the nature and habitability of the Sun seem ludicrous nowadays—and they are certainly far wider of the mark than most of his explorations into the unknown—there is this to be said for them: they were justified by the observations available at the time, they presented the first co-ordinated picture of solar phenomena, and they were only proved to be untenable by the spectroscope half a century later. In the matter of the habitability of the Sun, Moon and planets,[1] Herschel was attuned to the philosophical mood of his day, which shrank from the idea of 'wasted' (i.e. uninhabited) worlds and of the Earth as the unique home of life in the universe.

It is a curious commentary on the chanciness of scientific progress that it was a small technical problem incidental to Herschel's solar observations, and not the observations themselves, that led him furthest along the path of discovery in this field. For it was while experimenting with methods of shielding the eye from the concentrated heat and glare at the eyepiece of a telescope pointed at the Sun, that he made his most important and fruitful contribution to physics: the discovery of infra-red radiation. Had he been less richly endowed with that insatiable curiosity which is among the most precious qualities of the research worker, he would have solved his practical problem of designing an effective solar eyepiece, and would never have explored that little extra distance nor rounded that one more corner behind which this notable discovery was awaiting him. As it was, his early investigations connected with the protection of his eye while observing the

[1] Writing in 1789, Herschel referred to the stars as 'These suns, every one of which is probably of as much consequence to a system of planets, satellites, and comets, as our own. . . .'

Sun uncovered some curious and unexpected facts which were an immediate challenge to his lust to *know*. In pursuing these he was led to the discovery which Count Rumford described as the most important since the time of Newton, and about which Sir Joseph Banks wrote to him, 'I hope you will not be affronted when I tell you that, highly as I prized the discovery of a new Planet, I consider the separation of heat from light as a discovery pregnant with more important additions to science'.

Between March and November 1800 Herschel presented to the Royal Society four papers dealing with his investigations into the nature and behaviour of radiant heat, and its relation to visible light. In the first of these papers he described how he had at various times experimented with glass filters of different colours to reduce the telescopic brilliance of the Sun. 'What appeared remarkable', he continued, 'was, that when I used some of them, I felt a sensation of heat, though I had but little light; while others gave me much light, with scarce any sensation of heat. Now, as in these different combinations the sun's image was also differently coloured, it occurred to me, that the prismatic rays might have the power of heating bodies very unequally distributed among them. . . . If certain colours should be more apt to occasion heat, others might, on the contrary, be more fit for vision, by possessing a superior illuminating power. At all events, it would be proper to recur to experiments for a decision.'

These experiments he proceeded to make. In the first series he spread out the Sun's light into its component colours by means of a prism; this spectrum was projected on to a board in which was cut a narrow slit through which the light of only a single colour could pass; a thermometer was mounted behind this screen in such a manner that its bulb lay in the path of the light passing through the slit; two other thermometers on either side of it, their bulbs in darkness, were used as controls. By exposing the thermometer for ten minutes to light of each colour of the spectrum in turn, Herschel at once found that his surmise was correct, and that the heating effect of the various colours was very unequal: under the red portion of the spectrum the temperature rose 7 degrees in ten minutes, under the green $3\frac{1}{2}$ degrees, and under the violet only 2 degrees.

He then planned a series of experiments to determine 'the aptness of the rays for giving distinct vision'. From these he learnt that the rays with the greatest illuminating power (or, as we should now say, the rays to which the human eye is most sensitive) are the yellow and yellow-green; on either side of this region of the spectrum their 'aptness for giving distinct vision' falls off progressively as the red and violet ends are approached. After describing a further series of twenty-seven experiments on the transmitting qualities of various coloured and smoked glasses, Herschel summarized his conclusions: Heat rays, like those of light, are refracted when they pass through a prism; they are, however, turned through a smaller angle than the visible light rays; the intensities of the heat and the light rays in different parts of the spectrum are very different from one another.

The existence of infra-red radiation (i.e. radiation lying beyond the red end of the visible spectrum—which is to say that it is invisible, although it can be detected by its heating effect) was already suspected by Herschel, as is shown by his surmise that the greatest intensity of the heating rays 'perhaps lies even a little beyond visible refraction. In this case, radiant heat will at least partly, if not chiefly, consist, if I may be permitted the expression, of invisible light'.

Finally he threw out one of those suggestive and extraordinary conjectures that seem to spring from a prophetic intuition: 'It may be pardonable if I digress for a moment, and remark, that the foregoing researches ought to lead us on to others. May not the chemical properties of the prismatic colours be as different as those which relate to light and heat?' In asking this question Herschel appears to anticipate by nearly half a century the discovery of the special sensitivity of the silver halides to blue, violet and ultra-violet light which is the basis of photography.

The refraction, or bending, of heat rays by a prism was next followed up in a series of experiments that were described to the Royal Society in April 1800. Mounting his three thermometers on a wheeled base, and projecting the Sun's spectrum on to the top of a table, Herschel investigated more thoroughly the heating effect of the different regions of the visible spectrum. No heat, he found, was detectable beyond the violet; as the thermometer bulb entered the visible range of the spectrum a small temperature rise was registered; progressively higher rises were recorded at every successive position of the thermometer from the violet to the red. Then came the definitive confirmation of the suspicion voiced in the earlier paper: when the thermometer carriage was pushed on further still, so that its bulb lay in darkness beyond the red end of the visible spectrum, a yet higher temperature was recorded. 'The four last experiments prove, that the maximum of the heating power is vested among the invisible rays. . . . We have traced these calorific rays throughout the whole extent of the prismatic spectrum . . . we have pursued them a considerable way beyond the *prismatic spectrum*, into an invisible state, still exerting their increasing energy, with a decrease of refrangibility up to the maximum of their power . . . after which, the invisible *thermometrical spectrum*, if I may so call it, soon vanished.' Thus was the infra-red discovered.

The remainder of Herschel's researches in this field were

directed to determining whether heat and light were essentially of the same or of different natures. He was not sure that solar heat and heat from, say, a domestic fire, were of the same kind, and he therefore set himself the task—as he put it to Sir Joseph Banks—of 'analising radiant heat, as well solar as culinary, every way'. The first part of *Experiments on the solar, and on the terrestrial Rays that occasion Heat*, read to the Royal Society in May 1800, described the twenty experiments whereby he proved that the heat radiation from the Sun, a coal fire, a candle and a red-hot poker, obeyed the same laws of reflection and refraction as visible light. The second part of the paper, read in November, described a mammoth series of 198 experiments investigating all aspects of the refraction, scattering and transmission of heat rays by a variety of transparent and translucent materials, and by liquids.

Herschel concluded his brilliantly organized investigation by discussing what conclusions could be drawn regarding the respective natures of heat and light. We now know that both —together with other radiations, such as the ultra-violet, radio and television waves—are forms of identically the same wave motion, only differing from one another in the matter of their wavelengths. Herschel, however, felt that the only conclusion to be drawn from the very unequal intensities of heat and light in different regions of the spectrum was that different types of corpuscle are involved—for, like most of his contemporaries, he subscribed to Newton's corpuscular theory, according to which light is transmitted as a stream of submicroscopic particles, rather than in the form of waves. This mistaken deduction from his experimental material is intelligible enough when viewed against the scientific background of his day, and it in no way detracts from the value of the discoveries themselves—which for the first time put heat radiation on the scientific map—nor from the great experimental skill and ingenuity that he had displayed in a field not strictly his own.

The wheel was brought full circle by a short paper written in May 1801, in which Herschel described what he considered to be the perfect solution of the original problem that had turned him aside on this so fruitful excursion into the realm of physics. This was a glass-sided trough containing a dilute solution of ink in water, which perfectly reduced both the heat and the brightness of the Sun's telescopic image.[1]

Another great field of astronomy which Herschel pioneered was that of stellar photometry, or the measurement of the brightness of the stars; this he found virtually untouched, and left firmly based on a vast mass of accurate observations. From his earliest days as an observer he had been interested by the phenomenon of stellar variation: the first paper that he submitted to the Royal Society (in 1780, while he was still living at Bath) was devoted to his observations of the variable star Mira; and in 1783 he gave Sir Joseph Banks a short account of his last four years' observations of Algol, a star in which widespread interest had been aroused at that time by Goodricke's suggestion that its variation was due to the periodic eclipsing of a large faint star by a smaller and brighter one which revolved round it. In addition to the handful of stars then known to vary in brightness fairly rapidly and fairly regularly, there were others which appeared to have brightened or faded more slowly during the course of centuries. Short period variation, like that of Mira, interested Herschel as an objective phenomenon demanding explanation, and in the same way that everything in the visible heavens interested him; but the slow and steady brightening or fading of certain

[1] It is sometimes incorrectly stated that all Herschel's mirrors were of speculum metal. In fact he made a number of glass mirrors which, backed with black velvet, he used for solar observation.

An 'island universe'; the spiral nebula NGC 5236. This is what our own Galaxy might look like if seen at a very great distance from a viewpoint to one side of its central plane

stars appeared to him to have a great and additional significance for the human race, for if our Sun were to develop such a tendency it might well mean the end of life on this planet.

At this time the scientific study of stellar variation was hamstrung by the chaotic state of the magnitude system of measuring and describing stellar brightness. This system (see p. 66) had been handed down from Ptolemy; and although it was officially in use there was no universally recognized standard, and no two observers agreed in the magnitude scales that they used. It was therefore virtually impossible to make direct comparisons between the observations of different observers, or to say that because the magnitudes that they might ascribe to a certain star were different, the star's brightness must have varied.

In 1794 Herschel decided that before any progress could be made this would have to be remedied, and from then until the end of 1797 the programme of sweeps was suspended while he collected the observational material for the four *Catalogues of comparative Brightness of Stars* which were published by the Royal Society in 1796, 1797 and 1799.[1] This work was of fundamental importance, and may be said to have placed the study of stellar brightness, and particularly of stellar variation, on a firm and rational footing.

In the introduction to the first catalogue Herschel described and condemned the current condition of magnitude estimates of stellar brightness, and proposed in its place a system of 'sequences' whereby each star is related to its neighbours in order of brightness, rather than directly to a scale of magnitudes. In this way he laid down an accurate photometry of nearly 3,000 stars. The accuracy of this work was for many years not properly appreciated, being no doubt disguised by

[1] Two further catalogues remained in manuscript until 1905.

the fact that his estimates were not expressed in magnitudes.[1] But towards the close of the century E. C. Pickering, whose great *Harvard Photometry* is the standard work to-day, re-examined Herschel's catalogues and showed that his observations were on the average accurate to about one-tenth of a magnitude—the smallest brightness-difference that the normal human eye can detect.

The introduction to the second catalogue, which was completed the same year, contains Herschel's observations of the star alpha Herculis (the discovery of whose variability had been announced in the first catalogue), and also his views as to the probable cause of short period variations of stellar brightness: 'The rotatory motion of stars upon their axes is a capital feature in their resemblance to the sun. It appears to me now, that we cannot refuse to admit such a motion, and that indeed it may be as evidently proved as the diurnal motion of the earth. Dark spots, or large portions of the surface, less luminous than the rest, turned alternately in certain directions, either towards or from us, will account for all the phaenomena of periodical changes in the lustre of the stars, so satisfactorily, that we certainly need not look out for any other cause.'

Herschel completed this intensive observational programme in almost exactly three years, and returned once more to his routine work of sweeping the heavens in pursuit of his cosmological studies; this was completed in 1802. He thereupon turned his attention once again to the study of double stars—of which, it will be remembered, he had already compiled two catalogues, in 1782 and 1784.

Herschel's interest had originally been attracted to double stars because he saw in them a possible means of solving the intractable problem of stellar distance. This would involve—

[1] It was not until after William's death that the magnitude scale was rationalized by, among others, his son John.

as Herschel then assumed to be the case, in the absence of contrary evidence—that all stars are of roughly the same order of actual brightness, and that therefore the fainter member of an unequal double star is much more distant than its brighter 'companion': the two stars would not in fact be companions in any true, spatial sense, but would merely happen to lie in nearly the same direction as seen from the Earth. It had been pointed out by Mayer, as early as 1776, that there was at least a theoretical possibility that some double stars are true binary systems whose components not only *look* near together but *are* near together in space. Herschel was fully aware of this possibility, but in the postscript to his first *Catalogue of Double Stars* (1782) he explained that he used the name 'double-star' in preference to 'companion' or 'satellite', 'because, in my opinion, it is much too soon to form any theories of small stars revolving round large ones, and therefore I thought it adviseable carefully to avoid any expression that might convey that idea'.

The first intimation that he had been forced to abandon the view that all double stars are optical doubles and nothing more, came in the introduction to his third catalogue of nebulae and clusters (1802); here he classified the contents of the sidereal universe into twelve categories, the second of which is 'Binary sidereal Systems, or double Stars'. After dealing with the theoretical possibility that some doubles really are twin-sun systems, the members of which are gravitationally connected, he went on to make the important announcement: 'It will not be necessary to insist any further on arguments drawn from calculation, as I shall soon communicate a series of observations made on double stars, whereby it will be seen, that *many of them have actually changed their situation with regard to each other, in a progressive course, denoting a periodical revolution round each other.*'

The promised communication was read to the Royal Society on 9th June 1803, under the title *Account of the Changes that have happened, during the last Twenty-five Years, in the relative Situation of Double-stars; with an Investigation of the Cause to which they are owing*. It described in detail how the component stars of six out of over fifty doubles had changed their relative positions since his original observation of them; and it was shown that these changes could only be explained as the mutual revolution of two gravitationally connected bodies about their common centre of gravity. A second paper, read to the Society a year later, continued and extended the investigation.

Thus Herschel proved the existence in the heavens of true binary stars—not single and isolated, but paired stars—and this must rank as one of his most distinguished achievements in the field of stellar astronomy. It was also the first direct observational proof that the Newtonian law of gravitation was applicable beyond the frontiers of the Solar System.

During the following year Herschel devoted much time to the re-examination of his earlier discoveries among double stars. His last scientific paper (printed in the *Philosophical Transactions* in 1821, little more than a year before his death) was a third catalogue of double stars, 145 in number; these had mostly been discovered during the 20-foot sweeps and the special examination of the ecliptic that he had undertaken between 1792 and 1795, though some were previously unpublished discoveries dating from his still earlier reviews of the heavens with the 7-foot Newtonian. Thus his work in the field of double-star astronomy spanned the whole of his long career as an observer. In all, he added 848 new double and multiple stars to the store of human knowledge.

In 1805 and 1806, soon after his demonstration of the existence of binary stars, Herschel returned to the problem of the

Sun's proper motion, and both extended and refined his earlier results. This work—which, chronologically, falls within the scope of the present chapter—has already been described in Chapter 8.

CHAPTER THIRTEEN

THE DEVELOPMENT OF HERSCHEL'S COSMOLOGY

The often-quoted words which open Herschel's great paper of 1811—'A knowledge of the construction of the heavens has always been the ultimate object of my observations'—lay bare the underlying impulse of his life as a working scientist. Notable and varied as were his contributions in other branches of knowledge—physics, the Solar System, the Sun and the stars as such, practical optics—it was to the widest aspects of cosmology, the far frontiers of human vision and understanding, that his mind constantly turned.

Some account of his first steps in opening up this field was given in Chapter 8, and it may be as well to summarize these very briefly. By 1785 his star gauges and his sweeps for nebulae had led him to the following conclusions: The universe of stars is not of infinite extent, but has a definite size, shape and structure; the stars, in fact, form a great cluster, the Galaxy, whose shape is roughly that of a convex lens; the Milky Way is thus an optical effect rather than the result of actual stellar crowding; under sufficient telescopic power, the so-called nebulae are resolvable into clusters of stars, and these are of the same status as the Galaxy—that is, 'island universes'.

These conclusions could only be deduced from his observations if certain assumptions were made. (1) That the distribution of stars throughout the Galaxy is more or less uniform—the validity of the outlines of the Galaxy as established by his star-gauging technique depended, as A. M. Clerke aptly put it, 'on the assumption that stellar crowding indicated, not more stars in a given space, but more space stocked in the same proportion with stars'. (2) That his 20-foot telescope was capable of penetrating to the edge of the Galaxy in all directions—for otherwise the derived outline would be dictated by the limitations of the telescope rather than by the Galaxy's actual frontiers. (3) That the stars are of roughly the same intrinsic brightness: on this assumption were based his estimates of relative distances in terms of the distance of Sirius. (4) That sufficient telescopic power would resolve all the so-called 'nebulae' into clusters of stars—the basis of the 'island universe' corollary of his disc theory of the Galaxy.

With the passing of years—and thirty-five years elapsed between his earliest sweeps and his last paper on the construction of the heavens—Hereschel's observations forced him to modify, and even wholly to reject, some of these early assumptions. His ideas about galactic structure were thereby modified and refined to a large extent; but it is misleading to picture Herschel at the close of his life as a pathetic old man with all his fine theories lying in ruins around him, every bit as ignorant of the 'Construction of the Heavens' as he was when he turned his first telescope to the skies.

That Herschel did not unravel all the intricacies of galactic structure *au premier coup*, and that his ideas showed a continuous development, is hardly surprising. Even to-day, when the main outlines of his cosmology have been confirmed and established beyond the possibility of reversal, the stellar universe still teems with problems and unanswered questions:

galactic exploration, initiated by Herschel, still continues, and its field is as apparently inexhaustible as it was 150 years ago.

In 1789, the year after his marriage, the *Catalogue of a second Thousand of new Nebulae and Clusters of Stars* was ready for presentation to the Royal Society. In the introduction Herschel drew attention to a particular characteristic of star clusters that he had noticed in hundreds of instances—namely, the tendency of the stars comprising a cluster to congregate more densely towards the cluster's centre than at its edges. This tendency towards central condensation must, Herschel argued, indicate the action of some centrally-directed force or forces.[1] 'Since then almost all the nebulae and clusters of stars I have seen, the number of which is not less than three and twenty hundred, are more condensed and brighter in the middle; and since, from every form, it is now equally apparent that the central accumulation or brightness must be the result of central powers, we may venture to affirm that this theory is no longer an unfounded hypothesis, but is fully established on grounds which cannot be overturned. Let us endeavour to make some use of this important view of the constructing cause, which can thus model sidereal systems. Perhaps, by placing before us the very extensive and varied collection of clusters, and nebulae furnished by my catalogues, we may be able to trace the progress of its operation, in the great laboratory of the Universe.'

Herschel saw quite clearly where this conception of the degree of condensation as an index of age was leading him. 'It is also highly probable that a continuation of such decreasing magnitudes, and encreasing compression, will justly account for the appearance of round, easily resolvable, nebulae;

[1] 'Whether I am right to use the plural number,—central powers,—or whether I ought only to say,—the known central force of gravity,—my conclusions will be equally valid.'

where there is almost a certainty of their being clusters of stars. And no Astronomer can hesitate to go still farther, and extend his surmises by imperceptible steps to other nebulae, that still preserve the same characteristics, with the only variations of vanishing brightness, and reduction of size.' His aim was nothing less than a complete theory of the evolution of nebulae and clusters.

This brilliant extension of his original investigations of the contemporary structure of the heavens, by the introduction of the time element and of a conception of the nature of the evolutionary forces moulding the physical universe, led Herschel on from the exploration of the *geography* of the Galaxy to that of its *history*: 'This method of viewing the heavens seems to throw them into a new kind of light. They now are seen to resemble a luxuriant garden, which contains the greatest variety of productions, in different flourishing beds; and one advantage we may at least reap from it is, that we can, as it were, extend the range of our experience to an immense duration. For . . . is it not almost the same thing, whether we live successively to witness the germination, blooming, foliage, fecundity, fading, withering, and corruption of a plant, or whether a vast number of specimens, selected from every stage through which the plant passes in the course of its existence, be brought at once to our view?'

In the following year (1790) Herschel's concern with the growth and development of the physical universe received a powerful impetus from a totally different source. It will be remembered that as early as 1785 he had suspected that the planetary nebulae perhaps constituted an exception to his belief that *all* nebulae are resolvable into stars; on this belief he based his conception of island universes. During the intervening fifteen years his sweeps had turned up a number of other objects which seemed difficult to interpret as unresolved masses of stars. These objects were of the type known as nebulous stars (stars with 'milky chevelures', as Herschel more picturesquely described them): that is, stars surrounded by a patch of nebulosity resembling an enormously inflated atmosphere. Then on 13th November 1790, he discovered the object which later figured in his catalogue as IV 69. 'A most singular phenomenon!' he recorded. 'A star of about the 8th magnitude, with a faint luminous atmosphere, of a circular form, and of about 3 in′ diameter. The star is perfectly in the centre, and the atmosphere is so diluted, faint, and equal throughout, that there can be no surmise of its consisting of stars.'

This nebulosity surrounding the star must, he argued, consist of 'a shining fluid, of a nature totally unknown to us'. Otherwise one of two things must be true: either the central star is of normal size, in which case the stars composing its 'atmosphere' must be of quite unstellar smallness to remain invisible; or the 'atmosphere' consists of a cloud of normal-sized stars, in which case they must be very distant to remain unresolved, and the central star must then be of quite unstellar largeness. Herschel did not feel justified in making either of these assumptions without further evidence. It was preferable, he felt, to regard the 'chevelure' surrounding the central star as *true nebulosity*: what we know to be a structureless cloud of gas and dust, and what Herschel described as a shining fluid.

How did this discovery affect the hypothesis of island universes? Herschel's main reason for holding that 'all very faint milky nebulosity ought to be ascribed to an assemblage of stars', was the difficulty of accounting otherwise for its visibility at immense distances. But now that there was independent evidence that such non-stellar matter did exist, and was luminous enough to be visible, this difficulty vanished. He did not, however, immediately fly to the other extreme of believing that *no* nebula could be regarded as an assemblage of stars. All he conceded, with characteristic caution, was 'Perhaps it has been too hastily surmised that all milky nebulosity, of which there is so much in the heavens, is owing to starlight only'. In his paper of 1802 he still specifically stated that nebulae are 'perhaps to be resolved' into stars, and it seems certain that he continued to believe in the existence of island universes to the end of his life. Indeed, it would have been surprising had he done otherwise, for as long as the Galaxy is regarded as an island of stars in an ocean of empty space, analogy (a form of reasoning to which Herschel was specially prone) would suggest the existence of other and similar islands.

The proof of the existence of true nebulous matter—matter in a structureless, formless state, not differentiated into stars—was a milestone both in the development of Herschel's ideas and in the history of astronomy. From it later spring Herschel's most far-reaching ideas concerning stellar evolution; the germ was already contained in his 1791 paper where, after he had given reasons for believing that some nebulosity at least is self-luminous, he went on to remark briefly, 'If, therefore, this matter is self-luminous, it seems more fit to produce a star by its condensation than to depend on the star for its existence'.

Herschel's third and last catalogue of previously unknown nebulae and clusters was read to the Royal Society nine years later, in 1802, a fortnight before he set off for Paris. Like its predecessor it was prefaced by some 'Remarks on the Construction of the Heavens'. These are chiefly of interest nowadays in showing that by this time Herschel had progressed far beyond his original position regarding the uniform distribution of the stars. Referring to the 'vast collections of small stars that are profusely scattered over the milky-way', he wrote 'on a very slight examination, it will appear that this immense starry aggregation is by no means uniform. The stars of which it is composed are very unequally scattered, and show evident marks of clustering together into many separate allotments.'

It has sometimes been suggested that since Herschel's disc theory of the Galaxy was based on the assumption of the uniform distribution of the stars composing it, his later recognition that this distribution was in fact far from uniform meant that the theory itself had become untenable and was abandoned by him. Neither of these suggestions is true. From the very beginning Herschel had emphasized that his assumed uniformity of distribution was at best a statistical one, which allowed for the occurrence of many minor divergencies from strict regularity within a framework of over-all uniformity; and in the very paper which presented his disc theory to the world he spoke of the two or three hundred 'gathering clusters' of stars that he had observed within the Milky Way. The assumption of an approximate, large-scale uniformity of stellar distribution did not exclude the possibility of considerable non-uniformity on a smaller scale. All that was required to justify his deductions was that the occurrence of these local irregularities should itself be regular—that they should occur more or less uniformly in all parts of the Galaxy. Providing the *entire* Galaxy were composed of clouds and clusterings of stars, rather than 'insulated stars', then the issue would not be affected: gauges on a wide enough scale to smooth out these small-scale irregularities would still reveal the disc-like structure of the Galaxy; the Milky Way would still be primarily an optical effect, explicable in terms of the disc theory in preference to the ring theory.

Concerning nebulous stars, Herschel wrote in the introduction to his third catalogue, 'The nature of these remarkable objects is enveloped in much obscurity. It will probably require ages of observations, before we can be enabled to form a proper estimate of their condition [as no doubt it would have done, but for the invention of the spectroscope]. That stars should have visible atmospheres, of such an extent . . . is truly surprising, unless we attribute to such atmospheres, the quality of self-luminous milky nebulosity. We can have no reason to doubt of the starry nature of the central point . . . but, when the great distance of such stars is taken into consideration, the real extent of the surrounding nebulosity is truly wonderful.'

It is also interesting to see from this paper that by 1802 Herschel had come round to the view that the planetary nebulae—which had long been a source of puzzlement to him—are truly nebular objects (gaseous, that is to say, rather than stellar). And there is an interesting suggestion about the relation of these objects to nebulous stars which is a forward-looking hint of the cosmogony which he was to develop in great detail in the papers of 1811 and 1814: 'If we might suppose that a gradual condensation of the nebulosity about a nebulous star could take place, this would be one of them [i.e. a planetary nebula, many of which have central stars], in a very advanced state of compression.'

It can thus be seen that the papers since 1784 contain numerous indications that ideas on the evolutionary aspect of the cosmos were stirring in Herschel's mind. These ideas, slow to mature, were displayed as a fully developed and widely applied cosmogony in his next two papers (1811 and 1814). The conception of diffuse nebulous material as the birthplace of individual bodies such as planets and stars is usually attributed, under the name of the Nebular Hypothesis, to Laplace, who described such a cosmogony in his *Système du Monde*, published in 1796. We have seen, however, that the basic idea was already in Herschel's mind several years earlier, and was specifically though passingly mentioned in his 1791 paper on nebulous stars.

The 1811 paper—*Astronomical Observations relating to the Construction of the Heavens, arranged for the Purpose of a critical Examination, the Result of which appears to throw some new Light upon the Organization of the celestial Bodies*—and that of 1814—*Astronomical Observations relating to the sidereal part of the Heavens, and its Connection with the nebulous part; arranged for the purpose of a critical Examination*—must be reckoned among the very finest of Herschel's intellectual achievements. They exemplify with perfect clarity his ability to organize vast masses of observational material, and his far-reaching but never uncontrolled imaginative power. They were, too, the outcome of the intimate fusion of observation and interpretation which is a characteristic of all Herschel's work. Interpretation is never allowed to outrun observation, but at the same time he was always aware of the significance and possible or probable meaning of what he saw even while his eye was at the telescope.

The earlier paper deals primarily with the evolution of nebulae. Herschel started by admitting that in the course of years his ideas had developed in step with his observations, and that some of his earlier assumptions had had to be thrown overboard. 'If it should be remarked that . . . I am not entirely consistent with what I have already in former papers said on the nature of some objects that have come under my observation, I must freely confess that by continuing my sweeps of the heavens my opinion of the arrangement of the stars and their magnitudes, and of some other particulars, has undergone a gradual change; and indeed when the novelty of the subject is considered, we cannot be surprised that many things formerly taken for granted, should on examination prove to be different from what they were generally, but incautiously, supposed to be. For instance, an equal scattering of the stars may be admitted in certain calculations; but when we examine the milky way, or the closely compressed clusters of stars . . . this supposed equality of scattering must be given up. We may also have surmised nebulae to be no other than clusters of stars disguised by their very great distance, but a longer experience and better acquaintance with the nature of nebulae, will not allow a general admission of such a principle, although undoubtedly a cluster of stars may assume a nebulous appearance when it is too remote for us to discern the stars of which it is composed.' This is a very important statement, for it clearly shows that at this late stage in his career Herschel still admitted the usefulness of the uniformity-of-distribution assumption for certain restricted purposes and that he still recognized some nebulae, though not all, as being island universes.

He then went on to arrange the many different types of nebulae that he had observed into thirty-one groups, in such a way that the transition from any one group to the next was almost imperceptible. The whole series could then be interpreted as one of continuous development: 'It will be found that those contained in one article, are so closely allied to those in the next, that there is perhaps not so much difference between them, if I may use the comparison, as there would be in an annual description of the human figure, were it given from the birth of a child till he comes to be a man in his prime.' The mainspring and generating impulse of this development is progressive condensation, under the stress of gravitation. At the beginning of the series are various types of widespread and quite structureless nebulosity; next come diffuse nebulae which show faint traces of condensation; then smaller nebulae of increasing roundness and regularity of outline; then round nebulae with increasing central condensation, leading finally to small round nebulae with stellar nuclei, and 'stellar nebulae'.

The beginning and the end points of this sequence—vast, amorphous, undifferentiated clouds of gas on the one hand, and tiny patches of nebulosity constituting in effect the swollen atmosphere of a single star, on the other—are thus very different. Referring to this, Herschel pointed out that 'the total dissimilitude between the appearance of a diffusion of the nebulous matter and of a star, is so striking, that an idea of the conversion of the one into the other can hardly occur to anyone who has not before him the result of the critical examination of the nebulous system which has been displayed in this paper. The end I have had in view, by arranging my observations in the order in which they have been placed, has been to show, that the above mentioned extremes may be connected by such nearly allied intermediate steps, as will make it highly probable that every succeeding state of the nebulous matter is the result of the action of gravitation upon it while in a foregoing one, and by such steps the successive condensation of it has been brought up to the planetary condition [i.e. planetary nebula]. From this the transit to the stellar form, it has been shown, requires but a very small additional compression of the nebulous matter, and several instances have been given which connect the planetary to the stellar appearance.'

Having thus brilliantly, and with immense and detailed support from observation, dealt with the evolutionary sequence of the nebulae, Herschel in 1814 went on to apply similar principles to the evolution of star clusters, and to develop further his ideas on the birth of stars from nebulae. The latter process, which had been hinted at in many of his earlier papers, was represented in 1811 as being the end-point of nebular condensation: speaking of the planetary nebulae, he had written 'We may conceive that, perhaps in progress of time these nebulae which are already in such a state of compression, may be still farther condensed so as actually to become stars'.

Astronomical Observations relating to the sidereal part of the Heavens opens with a plain statement of its aims and purpose: 'In my paper of observations of the nebulous part of the heavens, I have endeavoured to shew the probability of a gradual conversion of the nebulous matter into the sidereal appearance. The observations contained in this paper are intended to display the sidereal part of the heavens, and also to show the intimate connection between the two opposite extremes, one of which is the immensity of the widely diffused and seemingly chaotic nebulous matter; and the other, the highly complicated and most artificially constructed globular clusters of compressed stars. The proof of an intimate connection between these extremes will greatly support the probability of the conversion of the one into the other.'

His first concern was to present examples of stars whose close association with nebulosity suggests that they had been developed from the nebulosity by a process of progressive condensation. Referring to some of these, he wrote, 'It would follow, that if the nebulosity should subside into the star, as seems to be indicated by the assumed form of the . . . nebulae, the star would receive an increase of matter proportional to the magnitude and density of the nebulosity in contact with it. This would give us the idea of what might be called the *growth* of stars.' And again: 'Here again the visible effect of gravitation supports the idea of the *growth* of stars by the gradual access of nebulous matter.'

Finally, apropos of a star situated on a general faintly nebulous background of wide extent, a star which has a nebulous 'chevelure' brighter than this background but fading into it by imperceptible degrees: 'The formation of these objects . . . manifests the affinity between the matter of which stars are composed, and that of the most unshapen chaotic mass of nebulosity. For the vanishing chevelure of a star being equally connected . . . with the generally diffused nebulous matter, and . . . with the star itself, round which it is in a state of gradual condensation; this double union denotes the mutual gravitation of the whole mass of nebulosity and the star towards each other; and, unless this proof can be invalidated, we must admit the fact of the growing condition of stars. . . . This argument also adds greatly to the probability of stars being originally formed by a condensation of the nebulous matter. . . . Moreover, the affinity between the nebulous and sidereal condition being established by these observations, we may be permitted to conceive both the generation and growth of stars, as the legitimate effects of the law of gravitation.'

Having established to his satisfaction this evolutionary connexion between nebulae and stars, Herschel went on to discuss the evolution of condensed globular clusters from more open, irregular and dispersed clusters. He then showed how the two processes may be combined: 'I have hitherto only considered the arrangement of stars in clusters with a view to point out that they are drawn together by a clustering power, in the same manner as the nebulous matter has, in my former paper, been proved to be condensed by the gravitating principle; but . . . we shall see that it is one and the same power uniformly exerted which first condenses nebulous matter into stars, and afterwards draws them together into clusters, and which by a continuance of its action gradually increases the compression of the stars that form the clusters.'

In these two papers Herschel succeeded in erecting an immense, detailed and dovetailed scheme of evolution which introduced order into the multitudinous variety of the nebulae and star clusters, and established a definite relationship between nebulae, clusters, and stars. Yet the foundation stone of this great structure was no more than the assumption that material particles, whether these are the tiny particles of a cloud of nebulous material, or the individual stars in a cloud of stars, will tend to condense under the action of gravitation.

When he applied the same principles to the Galaxy itself, Herschel was forced to envisage its progressive break-up into individual clusterings of stars, so that their general distribution would become less and less uniform. 'It is . . . evident, that if it [the Milky Way] ever consisted of equally scattered stars, it does so no longer. . . . The observations detailed in the preceding pages . . . authorize us to anticipate the breaking up of the milky way, in all its minute parts, as the unavoidable consequence of the clustering power arising out of those preponderating attractions which have been shewn to be everywhere existing in its compass." Looking into the far distant future he foresaw that 'the milky way must be finally broken up, and cease to be a stratum of scattered stars'.

His final paragraph is an example of that sort of luminosity of thought which continually delights the reader of Herschel's scientific papers: 'We may also draw a very important additional conclusion from the gradual dissolution of the milky way; for the state into which the incessant action of the clustering power has brought it at present, is a kind of chronometer that may be used to measure the time of its past and future existence; and although we do not know the rate of going of this mysterious chronometer, it is nevertheless certain, that since the breaking up of the parts of the milky way affords a proof that it cannot last for ever, it equally bears witness that its past duration cannot be admitted to be infinite.'

During 1813 and 1814 Herschel, then 76 years of age, was engaged in developing an entirely new method of star gauging. The obvious inequalities of stellar distribution meant that his original method of star-counts, while adequate for revealing the general and over-all shape of the Galaxy, could not be successfully applied to any particular region of small extent. Herschel, whose ingenuity showed no signs of flagging as the years of his old age advanced, worked out a system of gauging by limiting magnitudes, in an attempt to get over this restriction. Even if one assumes quite wide differences of actual brightness among the stars, it is still true to say that the average distance of, say, all stars of the 6th magnitude is greater than that of all the 1st magnitude stars. Whereas his original method of gauging consisted in observing many regions of the sky with the same telescopic power, and counting the total number of stars visible in many different equal-sized fields, the new one consisted in observing a single field with different telescopic powers. These were provided by two telescopes, the aperture of one of which was variable by means of diaphragms of accurately calculated diameters; the two telescopes, used as a unit, constituted an instrument whereby the number of stars of each successive magnitude could be counted. These relative numbers would then, Herschel argued, indicate the profundity of the star-populated space in this particular direction.

The 1817 paper, *Astronomical observations and experiments tending to investigate the local arrangement of the celestial bodies in space, and to determine the extent and condition of the Milky Way*, described Herschel's development of this method, and its application to the Milky Way as a whole. There is no doubt that the method of limiting magnitudes is statistically valid, and in a more refined form than Herschel's it was used by Seeliger towards the end of the century to confirm the disc theory in its general outlines. But great care has to be taken in its use, and it is doubtful whether—as applied by Herschel, and assuming general stellar luminosities comparable with that of Sirius—it could yield trustworthy results.

However, that may be, in 1817 Herschel was confirmed in his belief that the Sun is one of many millions of stars which together form a roughly disc-shaped system. This conclusion was strengthened in his last published paper on cosmology, the following year; this dealt with the application of his new gauging method to the determination of the relative distances of star clusters. The structure of the Galaxy was, he realized, very much more complex than he had originally supposed. His final view also envisaged a far greater extension of the Galaxy in its median plane than he had once thought possible: the stars of the Milky Way, that is to say, recede to greater depths of space than his first series of star gauges had suggested. In fact he was forced to the conclusion that, in certain directions, not even his 40-foot was capable of penetrating to the frontier of the Milky Way. Nevertheless, he did not consider our Galaxy unique, but continued to the end of his life in the belief that there exist island universes which are external to it; he still regarded many 'nebulae' as being truly stellar in character.

As his observational acquaintance with the universe of stars, nebulae and clusters deepened, during the long span of thirty-six years that separated his first and last papers on cosmology, Herschel was thus forced to modify and refine many of his early ideas. But the fundamental conclusions remained unaltered. And these conclusions have been confirmed by every subsequent worker, and have long since taken their place in the great body of established astronomical knowledge.

CHAPTER FOURTEEN

THE LAST TWENTY YEARS

Shortly after William and his little party returned to England from their holiday in Paris in 1802, the affairs of the Herschel family were once again to become embroiled with the wider issues of European politics. Napoleon's ambitions ranged further afield than the First Consulship of the French Republic, and in the following May England again found herself at war with France. A month later Hanover was occupied by the Napoleonic armies. Dietrich—who was still a member of the Court orchestra at Hanover, and now had a flourishing private practice as a teacher—wrote long and graphic letters to William during the ensuing years, describing the hardships suffered by the Hanoverians first under the French, and then under the Prussians, who had thrown in their lot with Napoleon. In the summer of 1806 he managed to slip away to England, and for a few weeks the three brothers (for Alexander came up from Bath for the occasion) were united again.

But conditions in Hanover went from bad to worse, and by 1808 Dietrich found himself deprived both of his savings and his livelihood. In order to support his wife and daughter he was forced to return to England to find employment.

After a short stay at Slough he settled in London, and here he remained for four years, until Napoleon's defeat at the hands of the Russians and the prospect of the speedy liberation of Hanover made it possible for him to return home. His sojourn in England had caused Caroline much worry and anxiety, for 'he came ruined in health, spirit and fortune, and according to the old Hannoverian custom, I was the only one from whom all domestic comforts were expected'.

It was only grudgingly that William Herschel, who throughout his long life had been so strenuous a worker, made any concessions to the advance of old age. The completion of the great programme of sweeps with the 20-foot reflector in 1802 marked some slackening of the tempo of his observational work. In 1808 he fell seriously ill, and for a time his life was despaired of; he recovered, but he could no longer ignore the fact that he was now an old man, and one, moreover, who had for years consistently over-worked himself.

In each of the three years following his break-down William made long holiday excursions in the north. In 1809, accompanied by his wife, John, and Sophia Baldwin, he visited the Lake District, and on the return journey through Yorkshire called at Leeds on his old friend Mr. Bulman, whose lodger he had been forty-seven years before. The party spent some days in Cambridge, which were mostly devoted to finding rooms for Mary Herschel when she returned with John at the beginning of the next term. For John Herschel—whose early education, after a brief spell at Eton, had been undertaken at a private school near Slough, and supplemented by tuition from a Scots mathematician named Rogers—was shortly to embark on his brilliant academic career as an undergraduate of St. John's College.

During William's absence Dietrich had kept Caroline company at Slough, and he stayed on there until in December his musical engagements forced him to return to London. Caroline, too, was beginning to feel the effects of age, and the daily walk from Upton (where, for several years, she had been lodging) was becoming increasingly inconvenient and difficult, especially in bad weather. In February 1809 'I sprained my ankle in coming home in the evening from Slough by attempting to walk through the snow in pattons. My brother was obliged to send me work to Upton, for it was not till a fourth-night after before I could walk there again.'

The following summer William, Mary and John went off on another long tour of the north, spending several days with James Watt near Birmingham before going on to Glasgow and Edinburgh. The next year they again visited Scotland, taking in the Lakes on the way; and, indeed, each year now saw William spending a holiday away from Slough. Sometimes he would visit friends, such as Dr. (now Sir) William Watson at Bath; several times he stayed at Dawlish, on the Devon coast, and at Ramsgate in Kent; often he would move from place to place. In 1813 he made a tour of the south coast with Mary and John, travelling through Kent, Sussex and Hampshire. This was the occasion of his meeting at Brighton with Thomas Campbell, the poet, critic and editor. Campbell, in a letter written to a friend, provides a glimpse of Herschel in his seventy-sixth year: 'Now for the old Astronomer himself; his simplicity, his kindness, his anecdotes, his readiness to explain and make perfectly perspicuous too his own sublime conceptions of the universe are indescribably charming. He is 76, but fresh and stout, and there he sat nearest the door at his friend's house, alternately smiling at a joke, or contentedly sitting without share or notice in the conversation. . . . Then, speaking of himself, he said, with a modesty of manner which quite overcame me, when taken with the greatness of the assertion: "I have looked further into space than ever human being did before me. I have observed stars of which the light, it can be proved, must take two million years to reach the earth." '

John Herschel, who had celebrated his twenty-first birthday earlier in the year, was described by Campbell as 'a prodigy in science and fond of poetry, but very unassuming'. The 'prodigy' had, indeed, but recently carried off the highest honours at Cambridge, where he had graduated as Senior Wrangler, won the Smith Prize, and been elected to a fellowship in his own college; this had been followed, at a phenomenally early age, by his election as Fellow of the Royal Society.

William's wish was that his son should enter the Church, but John's own inclinations were towards the Law, and early in 1814 he was enrolled as a student at Lincoln's Inn. In view of the brilliance of his mathematical career at Cambridge—and (if we may be wise after the event) in view of his subsequent distinguished career in astronomy—it may seem strange that he ever considered the Law as a profession. But, in the event, he was not destined for the Bar: the influence of such scientific friends as Wollaston and James South (with whom he later collaborated in observing double stars), and possibly his not very robust health, persuaded him to abandon his legal studies after little more than a year. His decision, in 1816, to follow in his father's footsteps strikes one now as being a bow to the inevitable. It seems, however, that at the time he would have preferred to have taken up once again the strands of his academic career at St. John's, and that his decision to bury himself at Slough as his father's assistant was dictated more by a sense of filial obligation than by natural inclination.

The occasions on which Caroline broke away from the quiet repetitions of her daily routine at Slough were infrequent enough to justify at least passing mention. The last of these rare holidays occurred in the spring of 1813, a couple of months after John's twenty-first birthday, when she went up to London to pay a long-promised visit to her friend Mrs. Goltermann. During the week that she was in town she saw something of such old friends as Fanny Burney (then Mme d'Arblay), Sir William and Lady Watson, Mrs. Maskelyne (Nevil Maskelyne had died two years before); and she called twice on Mme. Beckedorff at Buckingham Palace, where also she was received with great kindness by the Queen and Princesses.

One of the penalties of old age is the dropping off, one by one, of lifelong friends. The death in 1805 of Alexander Aubert ('the astronomical Mr. Aubert', as Herschel called him in one of his papers) severed a friendship that went back over twenty-five years. Maskelyne (succeeded at Greenwich by Pond) and Patrick Wilson both died in 1811, and James Watt—who in latter years had been, with his wife, a frequent visitor to Slough—in 1819. In 1814 William heard by chance of the death, some seven years previously, of his old friend and travelling companion General Komarzewsky, with whom he seems to have lost touch since the resumption of the French wars in 1803. For the same reason his previously lavish correspondence with Schröter had been largely cut off since 1803, and the possibility of its renewal vanished with Schröter's tragic death in 1816: three years previously his observatory at Lilienthal had been destroyed by the French troops, and the accumulated records of a lifetime's observations burnt—an indefensible act of barbarism from which the old man never recovered.

Around the turn of the century Herschel was still considerably occupied with his telescope-making activities: he had, then, only recently completed his second largest instrument—the 25-foot, with a mirror 24 inches in diameter, built for the King of Spain—and the 10-foot reflector of the same large aperture which was later sold to Lucien Bonaparte. From about 1807 to 1810 he was much involved in a series of experiments, and in preparing the three papers describing them, on the optical phenomenon known as Newton's rings. He began by giving his reasons for being dissatisfied with Newton's account of the formation of these alternate rings of light and darkness between closely adjacent surfaces, such as those of the components of the compound lens. He then went on to develop a theory of his own to account for them. This was justly criticized by the Publications Committee of the Royal Society and, after its publication, by the scientific world at large. Herschel replied to his critics with some heat, and the ensuing controversy undoubtedly contributed to his breakdown in 1808. The smoke of controversy has long since cleared, and we can now see that Herschel in this investigation ventured on to highly technical ground without the specialized knowledge that would have saved him from going astray. (The correct interpretation of this aspect of the behaviour of light, in terms of the interference of one wave system with another, had actually been made by Young in 1801, though it was not until its revival by Fresnel in 1815 that it became widely known.)

Herschel's venture into a field so alien to his own sprang from his inability to leave uninvestigated any mysterious or unexplained object or phenomenon that he might encounter. Dr. Dreyer has given a fair and balanced summing up of this episode in Herschel's life: 'This was the only occasion on which Herschel published a paper on an important subject which did not throw out ideas destined to influence the trend of scientific progress. It shows that his mind did not recognize its own limitations; but this very circumstance was an important factor in encouraging him to set forth views on the construction of the heavens which continued to prevail during the following century. A more cautious mind would have perceived that questions connected with the nature of light lay outside its proper sphere; but it might also have recoiled from venturing without any guidance from previous investigators to attack the deepest problems of sidereal astronomy . . . but the genius of Herschel, which acknowledged no boundaries to its explorations, planned work on original lines and found untrodden paths.'

William's gradually failing health and strength are witnessed by Caroline's diary for 1814 and 1815. The winter of 1813 had been unusually severe, most of western Europe being almost continuously frost-bound for three months;[1] 'my Brother suffering from indisposition, and I, for my part, felt I should never be anything else but an Invalid for life, but which I very carefully kept to myself, as I wished to be useful to my Brother as long as I possibly could.' In April he paid Alexander a short visit, setting out with a bad cough which the journey by stage coach did nothing to improve; and it was not until the coming of warmer weather that he was fully recovered. At the end of Alexander's visit to Slough the following summer, Caroline wrote sadly, 'Alex left Slough, my eldest Brother with him, going on for Dawlish to recruit his strength again. His declining health had a sad effect on Alexander's spirits and I was in continual fear of the consequence, for nothing but the thoughts of the yearly meeting had till then kept up his spirits. . . . My Brother came home [from Dawlish] having a violent cough. The latter end of August my Nephew came home very unwell and the Phisi-

[1] In a paper read to the Royal Society in February 1814, Herschel gave as one of his reasons for his comparatively infrequent use of the 40-foot that it was often put out of commission by dew forming on its speculum, 'and in cold weather by freezing upon it for the whole night, and even for weeks together'.

cians ordered him to the sea-side . . . and I went the same day to be with my Brother. . . . The first fourthnight of my being with him he was not able to do anything which required strength.'

In February 1816 news came from Bath that Alexander had had an accident in which he had injured his leg, and that he was confined to his bed on a diet of 'bread and butter, Barly water and water grewel and Tee and that very sparingly'. It soon became clear that Alexander's working days were finished (he was then over seventy); Bath no longer had any ties for him, and he decided to return to Hanover and make his home with Dietrich. The parting from his brother and sister was a sad one. For thirty-five years he and William had been in England together: even after William's removal to Slough, Alexander's annual visits had been a constant feature of their family life, and many were the hours that he had spent helping William in the workshop. On 2nd September 1816, Caroline said good-bye to Alexander on board his ship at Wapping. (William had made his farewells at Slough, before setting off for a rest and a change of air at Dawlish with John.) Neither Caroline nor William were to see Alexander again, for he died in 1821, the year before Caroline herself returned to Hanover.

The honours of the scientific world had accumulated round Herschel with the passing of the years, as the learned societies, academies and universities of all Europe conferred their recognitions upon him. In 1816 he was created a Knight of the Hanoverian Guelphic Order by the Prince Regent—a tardy and hardly adequate recognition of the great glories that her adopted son had added to British science.

In 1819 Caroline was deprived of another old and dear friend, who was one of her few remaining links with the distant past in Hanover: Queen Charlotte having died the previous year, her household at Windsor was disbanded, and Mme Beckedorff and her daughter returned to their native Hanover. In the same year Sophia Baldwin left the Herschel household, of which she had been a more or less constant member since William's marriage, to become the wife of a Mr. Beckwith. Her married life was tragically short, however, for she died of consumption the following year, and her baby, who was entrusted to the care of Lady Herschel, only survived her by a matter of months.

A fortnight or so after Sophia's wedding, Sir William and Lady Herschel set off on a short visit to Bath. The preceding winter had also been one of abnormally low temperatures (with ice on the Thames at Kew nineteen feet thick), and William's health was once again causing anxiety: it must by now have been as apparent to his wife as it was to his sister that his strength was slowly failing, and that he had not many more years to live. Once again—as during the old days at Bath—we can turn to Caroline's journal for the most vivid and authentic record of the daily life of the Herschel household. On 2nd April 1819, she wrote, 'My Brother left Slough accompanied by Lady H. for Bath, he being so very unwell and the constant complaint of giddiness in his head so much increased that they were obliged to be 4 nights on the road both going and coming. The last moments before he stept in the carriage were spent in walking with me through his Library and workrooms, pointing with anxious looks to every shelf and drawer, desiring me to examine all, and to make memorandums of them as well as I could. He was hardly able to support himself and his spirits so low, that I found difficulty in commanding my voice so far as to give him the assurance he should find on his return that my time had not been misspent. When I was left alone I found on looking around that I had no easy task to perform, for there were packs of writings to be examined which had not been looked at for the last 40 years. But I did not lose a single day without working in the Library as long as I could read a letter without candle-light, and taking with me copying, &c., &c., which employed me for best part of the night, and thus I was enabled to give my Brother a clear account of what had been done at his return on the 1st of May.' Writing to her from Bath, William told how 'I am just returned from a walk to New King Street, where I saw the House, No. 19, in the garden of which I discovered the Georgian Planet. For Bath news I must refer you to Lady Herschel, as I feel my wrist too feeble to guide the pen properly.'

Bath, indeed, had brought no improvement in his condition, and Caroline had to record, 'he came home much worse than he went, and for several days hardly noticed my handy-works'. On July 8th, she recorded briefly, 'We thought my Brother was dying. On the 9th he was persuaded to be blooded in the arm which something relieved him.' Only a few days before this relapse he had sent a note by hand to Caroline which shows how, despite everything, his heart was still in the heavens that he had so long, so assiduously, and so fruitfully observed: 'Lina, there is a great comet. I want you to assist me. Come to dine and spend the day here. If you can come soon after one o'clock we shall have time to prepare maps and telescopes. I saw its situation last night, it has a long tail.' Written across this is a note in Caroline's hand, 'I keep this as a Relic! every line *now* traced by the hand of my dear Brother becomes a treasure to me.'

The year 1820 brought in its train the deaths both of Sophia Beckwith and of Herschel's old patron, George III. In the same year the Astronomical Society (later to become the Royal Astronomical Society) was founded. The originator of the scheme was Dr. William Pearson, an amateur astronomer of some note whose two earlier attempts to organize a society of astronomers in 1812 and 1816 had come to nothing. The committee which he formed in 1820 to draft the constitution of the new Society included John Herschel and his friends of Cambridge days, Peacock and Babbage. In due course it was decided that the Duke of Somerset should be elected the first President (John Herschel being the Foreign Secretary, and William one of the Vice-Presidents). The Duke, however, declined the Presidency on the representations of Sir Joseph Banks, who saw in the formation of a separate Society devoted to astronomy a threat to the prestige of the Royal Society and to its 150-year-old claim to be the voice, fountain-head, and clearing house of all branches of British science. After an initial period during which the newly formed Society was without a President, William Herschel agreed to accept the office—on the clear understanding, however, that his Presidency must be purely nominal, as he was then too old and too weak to undertake personally the arduous duties that the office involved. And, in fact, although he remained President of the Astronomical Society until his death, he never attended one of its London meetings.

During 1820 he was engaged on his final task as a telescope maker—though now he could only work by proxy, and the actual grinding, figuring, polishing and assembly were carried out by John under his guidance. The result of this co-operation between father and son was the fine 20-foot instrument that was later to accompany John to the Cape.

The story of Herschel's last days was told by Caroline some eighteen months later, when she had established herself in Hanover and had 'acquired fortitude enough for noting down in my day book . . . those heartrending occurrences I was witnessing during the last 9 months of the 50 years I had lived in England'. The gloom of impending separation from the 'dearest and best of Brothers' to whom she had devoted her life, hung heavily over the winter of 1821 and the early months of the new year. By 21st June 1821, she had for the last time acted as William's assistant at the telescope. Now she wrote, 'During the day my time was spent in endeavours to support my dear Brother in his suffering decline. And besides the hope that we might continue yet a little longer together began to forsake me, for my own health and spirits were in that state that I was in dayly expectation of going before. Therefore each moment of separation from my dear Brother I spent in endeavours to arrange my affairs. . . . And for this purpose my thoughts were continually divided between my Brother's Library, from which I was now on the point of being severed for ever, and among my unfinished work at home endevouring to bring by degrees all into its proper place.'

Early in August 1822, John Herschel set out on a sight-seeing tour of the Low Countries, for his father appeared at that time to be in good enough health for immediate fears to be allayed. In July, indeed, Caroline had hopes of a real improvement—'I had a dawn of hope that my Brother might regain once more a little strength; for I have a memorandum in my almanack of his walking with a firmer step than usual—above three or four times the distance from the dwelling house to his library—in his garden, for the purpose to gather and eat Rasberries with me; but I never saw the like again.' The letters telling John of his father's final illness never caught up with him as he travelled from place to place on the Continent, and it was not until his return to England that he learned of his death.

On August 8th Caroline found her brother 'so languid that I thought it necessary to take soon a seemingly unconscious leave for the night'. It was her habit to pass a few hours with

William every morning, and on the 15th 'I hastened to the spot where I was wonted to find him with the newspaper which I was to read to him. But instead I found Mrs. Morsom, Miss Baldwin [Mary Baldwin, Sophia's sister] and Mr. Bulman from Leeds, the grandson of my Brother's earliest acquaintances in this country. . . . I was informed my Brother had been obliged to retire again to his room, where I flew immediately. Lady H. and the housekeeper were with him administering everything which could be thought of for supporting him. I found him much irritated at not being able to grant Mr. Bulman's request of obtaining a token of remembrance for his Father; but as soon as he saw me I was sent to the Library to fetch one of his last papers and a Plate of the 40 feet telescope. But for the universe could I not have looked twice at what I had snatched from the shelf, and when he faintly asked if the breaking up of the milky way was in it, I said "Yes!" and he looked content. . . . After half an hour's vain attempt of supporting himself, my Brother was obliged to consent to being put to bed, leaving no hope ever to see him rise again; and for 10 days and nights we remained in the most heart-rending situation till the 25 of August; when not one comfort was left to me but that of retiring to the chamber of death and there to ruminate without interruption on my isolated situation. And of this last solace I was robbed on the 7th September, when the dear Remains were consigned to the Grave.'

So, on Sunday, 25th August 1822, in the eighty-fourth year of his age, died William Herschel, 'Father of Stellar Astronomy' and one of the greatest explorers of all time.

CHAPTER FIFTEEN

POSTSCRIPT: CAROLINE AND JOHN

Though the death of William logically brings this story to an end, it is impossible to leave in mid-air the account of the work and lives of Caroline and John Herschel: of Caroline, because she had for so many years been William's right hand, working with him in a collaboration as close as that of Marie and Pierre Curie; of John, because his subsequent distinction in the world of science owed so much to the example and inspiration of his father; and of both Caroline and John, because after William Herschel's death they continued, extended, and in a sense completed the work that he had left unfinished.

The death of her brother washed out all meaning from Caroline's life. For her, as for Mary Herschel, bereavement was the irrevocable absence of someone dearly loved: but to this, in Caroline's case, was added the termination of that active co-operation which during the course of half a century had become more than a mere habit—it was a way of life, and the only one she could imagine. Since she had forsworn her own career as a singer, so many years before, she had been without personal ambition. Her cometary discoveries she made light of, counting them as nothing compared with the assistance that she had been able to give William. His interests, his work, his well-being, his reputation—these were her only concern.

The prospect of England without William was unbearable, and even before his death Caroline had decided that when at last she was alone she would return to her native Hanover. With a sort of desperate urgency she set about winding up her affairs at Slough; her one wish was to get away with the least possible delay. It had been arranged that she should make her home with Dietrich, and early in October he arrived at Slough to accompany her on her journey back to her birthplace. Caroline was then seventy-two years old, and in ill health; she felt that before she died she wanted to hear her native tongue spoken around her once again. Had she known that she still had twenty-five years of life before her—half the total period she had spent in England—she might perhaps have decided otherwise.

At 9 a.m. on 10th October 1822, Caroline climbed into the carriage and left Slough for ever; a few days in London, the passage to Rotterdam, and by the 28th she and Dietrich were in Hanover.

She found herself in a world of strangers. Even among her own relations, those of the younger generation had never met her before, and her contemporaries she found so changed as to be hardly recognizable. Anna Knipping, a widowed daughter of Dietrich, alone found a place in Caroline's affection-starved heart. She, indeed, became Caroline's closest and most cherished friend; Mme Beckedorff and her daughter were also a great comfort to her during what amounted to her exile in Hanover.

The years had not dealt kindly with Dietrich, 'who suffers very frequently much from weakness, so that to combat against infimities and peevishness (the usual companions of old age) depends entirely on my exertion to bear my share without communication, for unfortunately we are never in the same mind, and with a nervous person of an irritable temper one can only talk of the weather or the flavour of a dish, for which I care not a pin'.

Caroline, in fact, suffered horribly from loneliness, and time and time again she wished that she had never left England, where at least she would be near her adored nephew, whose personal affairs and steady progress to fame were now the chief interests of her life. 'Out of my family connections I can boast to possess the esteem and love of all who are great and good in Hanover', she wrote to Lady Herschel, 'but to a lonely old woman, who is seldom able to go into or to receive company, this does not compensate for the want of sympathizing relations.' So when, five years after her return to Hanover, Dietrich died—(leaving her the sole remaining member of her generation of Herschels)—she decided to move into lodgings on her own.

In the autumn of 1823 she once more took up the work on which she had already been engaged for a number of years: the reduction of all William's nebulae and clusters and their arrangement in a single catalogue by successive zones from the North Pole southward. This enormous undertaking was primarily designed to assist John in his work of reobserving all his father's discoveries; and in 1825 *A Catalogue of the Nebulae which have been observed by Wm Herschel in a Series of Sweeps; brought into Zones of N.P. Distance and order of R.A. for the year 1800* was completed and sent off to her nephew in England. Though it was never published, it proved invaluable to John in his survey of the northern heavens, and in 1828 it earned Caroline the Gold Medal of the Astronomical Society.

Further honours were heaped upon her aged shoulders. In 1835 she was elected an honorary member of the Royal Astronomical Society—a considerable distinction since membership was in those days open only to men—and three years later she was admitted to membership of the Royal Irish Academy. The Gold Medal for Science was awarded her by the King of Prussia in 1846, and the wording of the citation could not have been more accurately calculated to appeal to Caroline: 'In recognition of the valuable services rendered to Astronomy by you as the fellow-worker of your immortal brother, Sir William Herschel.'

Many visitors came to call on Caroline in her retirement—men of science such as Gauss, Humboldt and Mädler, as well as royalty who had known her during the Windsor days and whose many kindnesses now gave proof of the affection and respect that they felt for the venerable old lady. John visited her three times (accompanied on the last occasion, in 1838, by his five-year-old son William), and she corresponded regularly both with him and with his wife.

So the years passed. Caroline, indomitable as ever, retained her liveliness of mind and body to the last. Until she was nearly ninety she was a well-known figure at the theatre, and seldom missed a concert. On her 97th birthday she was visited by the Crown Prince and Princess, whom she entertained for two hours, even singing for them a catch that William had composed many years before.

She died within two months of her 98th birthday, on 9th January 1848, and was buried in the Gartenkirchhof near the place where the body of her father had been laid eighty-one years previously. The longevity of the Herschels was remarkable—the combined ages of William, Caroline and John Herschel make a total of 260 years.

POSTSCRIPT: CAROLINE AND JOHN

At the time of his father's death John Herschel had already been committed to a life of science for six years.

Whilst at Cambridge he and his two friends, Peacock and Babbage, had been instrumental in introducing into the University the continental calculus in place of Newton's much less flexible method of fluxions; he had been Senior Wrangler of his year; and in 1821 he was awarded the Royal Society's Copley Medal (which the discovery of Uranus had earned his father exactly forty years earlier) for the work that he had already done, at the age of twenty-nine, in the field of pure mathematics. This outstanding mathematical aptitude, combined with the example given him by his father, made it almost inevitable that he should take up astronomy as a career. His first undertaking was the reobservation and measurement of William Herschel's double stars. Experiments in physical optics and chemistry also occupied him during these early years, and in 1819 he discovered the method (still in use) of fixing photographic images by dissolving the unexposed silver salts with 'hypo'; twenty years later he obtained the first successful photographic negative on glass.

Between 1821 and 1823 he collaborated with James South—who had a finely equipped private observatory at Southwark—in a programme of measurements of double stars: work whose value was recognized by the award of the French Academy's Lalande Prize in 1825 and the Gold Medal of the Astronomical Society in the following year. During the early 1820's John made several fairly extensive tours of the Continent, on one of which (1824) he visited Caroline in Hanover—to the old lady's great delight.

From double stars he turned his attention to that field of observational astronomy that his father had made particularly his own—nebulae and clusters. 'I had the 20-feet directed on the nebulae in Virgo,' he wrote to his aunt in 1825, 'and determined afresh the Right ascensions and Polar distances of 36 of them. These curious objects (having now nearly finished the double stars) I shall now take into my special charge—nobody else can see them.' It was indeed true that until the completion of the Earl of Rosse's great 60-foot reflector in 1845, more than half William Herschel's 2,500 nebulae and clusters were effectively unobservable by any instrument but the 20-foot 'front view' telescope that John had made under his supervision in 1820.

By 1833 John had retraced his father's footsteps and had systematically swept the whole of the northern heavens. Considering that he had no faithful Caroline to assist him, but had to record and reduce all his observations himself, this was a remarkably speedy achievement. The fruits of this observational programme, carried out at Slough with his 20-foot reflector, were contained in the catalogue of 2,307 nebulae and clusters (525 of them his own discoveries) which was published by the Royal Society in 1833, and for which, three years later, he was awarded the Gold Medals of both the Royal Society and the Royal Astronomical Society. With the same fine 20-foot instrument he also discovered 3,347 double stars, which were reported to the Royal Astronomical Society in seven catalogues between 1826 and 1870;[1] in 1828 he observed the two satellites of Uranus, which had virtually been 'lost' since their discovery and initial study by his father.

His rapid recognition as an important figure in the scientific world was reflected in his appointment as Secretary of the Royal Society in 1824, and the offer (which he refused) of the Professorship of Mathematics at Cambridge two years later. On the coronation of William IV in 1831 he was created a Knight of the Guelphic Order.

[1] His great *General Catalogue of 10,300 Multiple and Double Stars* was published posthumously in 1874.

POSTSCRIPT: CAROLINE AND JOHN

In 1829 John Herschel married Margaret Brodie—an event that gave much pleasure and satisfaction to Caroline in her Hanoverian loneliness. His review of the northern heavens being completed, John had long cherished the ambition to round off his father's work by sweeping and gauging the southern regions of the sky that were unobservable from Slough. The death of his mother in 1832—up to which time he had lived with her at Slough—made it possible for him to realize this ambition. In June of that year he paid Caroline a visit, and in a letter to his wife described how 'I found my aunt wonderfully well and very nicely and comfortably lodged; and we have since been on the full trot. She runs about the town with me and skips up her two flights of stairs as light and fresh at least as *some folks* I could name who are not a fourth part of her age. . . . In the morning till eleven or twelve she is dull and weary, but as the day advances she gains life, and is quite 'fresh and funny' at ten or eleven p.m. and sings old hymns, nay even dances to the great delight of all who see her.' Caroline was then eighty-one.

At this time no systematic examination of the southern skies had been undertaken. John at first toyed with the idea of transporting his telescopes to Australia, but he finally decided on South Africa; and in November 1833 he sailed for the Cape with his wife and three children. With him, also, he took his 20-foot reflector, with three 18·7-inch mirrors, and a fine refractor. These he set up in the grounds of Feldhausen, an old Dutch colonial house situated not far from the foot of Table Mountain.

During the four happy years that he spent at the Cape, he completed an almost unbelievably extensive observational programme. His sweeps of the entire southern hemisphere of the heavens supplemented his own and his father's work at Slough, so that between them father and son examined telescopically every square degree of the heavens, and the northern hemisphere twice over. John Herschel must be the only man who ever covered the entire star sphere by visual observation. During this programme he discovered 1,202 double stars and 1,269 nebulae and clusters that had never before been catalogued or described.

He made the first thorough investigation of the Magellanic Clouds—those strange, misty patches which to the naked eye look like disconnected sections of the Milky Way, and are in fact independent galaxies which may be regarded as satellites of our own Galaxy—and catalogued 1,163 stars, nebulae and clusters in them.

He subjected the amazing nebula in Argo to an intensive study, cataloguing 1,203 galactic stars superimposed upon it; he observed, in 1837, a flare-up of the irregular variable eta Argus, whose behaviour somewhat resembles that of a recurrent nova. He continued his father's star gauges over the southern skies, counting 69,000 stars in 2,299 fields. These confirmed the main outlines of William Herschel's disc theory of the Galaxy, although later in his life John turned with favour to the ring theory.

His Cape observations of the Sun led him to evolve a cyclonic theory of sunspot formation. (At this time he still accepted his father's ideas concerning the nature of the Sun—as an at any rate potentially habitable globe—and it was not until 1864 that he adopted the idea of the Sun as a wholly gaseous and incandescent body.) He observed Mimas and Enceladus—the satellites of Saturn—for the first time since they had last been observed by William Herschel. And he made an extremely detailed series of observations of Halley's comet, which, at its second predicted return in 1835–6, underwent the most extraordinary changes of form; these John recorded in a classic series of drawings.

While at the Cape he received the Royal Astronomical Society's Gold Medal for his method of calculating the orbits of binary stars, and also the Gold Medals of both the Royal Society and the Royal Astronomical Society for his 1833 catalogue of northern nebulae and clusters. When he returned home in 1838 his reception was hardly less than triumphal. He was fêted and showered with awards and distinctions; he was offered, but refused, reimbursement by the Treasury for all the expenses of his expedition to the Cape; he likewise refused the representation of Cambridge University in Parliament, and the Presidency of the Royal Society, on the grounds that they would interfere too much with his scientific work; he was created a Baronet on the coronation of Queen Victoria; and he was awarded the honorary degree of Doctor of Civil Laws at Oxford University in the following year.

John Herschel whose observational career had up to this time been of such brilliance, never again put eye to telescope after his return from the Cape. His reputation led him to become involved in a variety of public duties which kept him fully engaged. From 1850 until his resignation five years later, he was Master of the Mint; he sat on Royal Commissions and on numerous scientific bodies; he undertook scientific work for the Government; he was one of the Trustees of the British Museum, three times President of the Royal Astronomical Society, and for many years a member of the Council of the Royal Society and of the Board of Visitors to the Royal Observatory. Every spare moment of the first nine years following his return from the Cape was, moreover, occupied with the enormous task of preparing his Cape observations for publication.

He and his family had settled down once again at Slough on their return from South Africa, and it was in the following year (1839) that he had his father's great 40-foot reflector dismantled. In 1840 he moved to Collingwood, a large country house at Hawkshurst in Kent, where he remained for the rest of his life, although his public duties involved frequent residence at his London house in Harley Street.

The publication of *Results of Astronomical Observations at the Cape of Good Hope* in 1847 won him the Copley Medal and came just in time for Caroline to receive a copy—a happy circumstance, for in it she saw the completion by her nephew of her brother's great project of a survey of the whole heavens.

Foremost among John Herschel's very numerous writings must be placed his *Outlines of Astronomy*. This book, an expansion of an earlier one written in 1833, was published in 1849 and achieved immediate and enormous popularity, becoming the standard general work for several generations. In 1855 he retired from public life, and devoted himself at Collingwood to the preparation of his *General Catalogue of Nebulae and Clusters*, which included every such object then known (to the number of 5,079) and which—in Dreyer's revision of 1888—is still the standard catalogue. From this gargantuan project he went on to the hardly less formidable one of consolidating in a single list all his father's double star discoveries. Further plans were cut short by his death in 1871. Replete in years and loaded with honours, Sir John Herschel was buried in Westminster Abbey, not far distant from the tomb of Newton.

The comparison of the careers of William and John Herschel makes an interesting study. John started life with every advantage; William with none. The elder Herschel not only had to teach himself everything beyond the simple syllabus of the Garrison School and the lessons of his old tutor Hofschläger, but he had also to make his own discovery of astronomy: and the transformation of the organist and choirmaster into the practising astronomer ran away with the first thirty-five years of his life. John, on the other hand, set out with the double advantage of outstanding natural mathematical abilities and a youth spent in the scientific environment of Slough, with the shining example of his father always before him. These were supplemented by a fine education, such as William never had.

Their working lives, too, described quite dissimilar patterns. William worked in retirement from the world (though the world flocked to his doorstep), and gave himself up utterly and wholly to his self-appointed task of unravelling the most obscure mysteries of the heavens. John suffered the penalties of early recognition as one of the foremost scientists of his day: the accumulation of appointments and public duties which, when he was only forty-six, put an end to his career as an observer.

John Herschel was the admirably equipped professional[1] astronomer. William, lacking both his mathematical prowess and his technical training, was always and essentially the amateur. But that William Herschel towered far above his son in mental stature and achievement can never be questioned. The son had ability, and to spare, but he lacked those qualities of greatness that so distinguished his father: the consuming driving urge to discover, to observe, to establish new *facts*; and the controlled power of imagination and untrammelled originality of thought which he brought to bear upon their interpretation. These justify the placing of William Herschel among the immortals.

John Herschel once truly remarked, in a letter to Caroline, 'Precision is more my aim than it was my father's, whose object was always discovery.'

[1] Though in fact he never occupied a paid position as an astronomer.

BIBLIOGRAPHY

Mrs. John Herschel, *Memoir and Correspondence of Caroline Herschel* (Murray, 1876).

C. A. Lubbock, *The Herschel Chronicle* (Cambridge University Press, 1933).

The Scientific Papers of Sir William Herschel (Royal Society and Royal Astronomical Society, 1912). Dr. J. L. E. Dreyer's [illegible] contains much valuable [illegible] William Herschel.

Reginald L. Waterfield, *A Hundred Years of Astronomy* (Duckworth, 1938).

From the vast literature devoted to twentieth-century cosmology, the following titles may be recommended:

B. J. Bok and Priscilla Bok, *The Milky Way* (Harvard Books on Astronomy, 1941).

Harlow Shapley, *Galaxies* (Harvard Books on Astronomy, 1943).

BIBLIOGRAPHY

Mrs. John Herschel, *Memoir and Correspondence of Caroline Herschel* (Murray, 1876).

C. A. Lubbock, *The Herschel Chronicle* (Cambridge University Press, 1933).

The Scientific Papers of Sir William Herschel (Royal Society and Royal Astronomical Society, 1912).

Dr. J. L. E. Dreyer's introduction to the *Scientific Papers* contains much valuable material about Herschel's optical work, as well as more general biographical data.

Reginald L. Waterfield, *A Hundred Years of Astronomy* (Duckworth, 1938).

Traces the development of astronomy during the century following Herschel's death, and should be referred to by anyone wishing to learn how Herschel's pioneer researches were extended by later astronomers.

From the vast literature devoted to twentieth-century cosmology, the following titles may be recommended:

B. J. Bok and Priscilla Bok, *The Milky Way* (Harvard Books on Astronomy, 1941).

Harlow Shapley, *Galaxies* (Harvard Books on Astronomy, 1943).

BIBLIOGRAPHY

Edwin Hubble, *The Realm of the Nebulae* (Oxford University Press, 1936).

Edwin Hubble, *The Observational Approach to Cosmology* (Clarendon Press, 1937).

A. S. Eddington, *The Expanding Universe* (Pelican Books, 1940).

F. J. Hargreaves, *The Size of the Universe* (Pelican Books, 1948).

Hector Macpherson, *Modern Cosmologies* (Oxford University Press, 1929).

INDEX

INDEX

INDEX

INDEX